TEACHER'S GUIDE

Connected Mathematics 2™

D1328195

Looking for Pythagoras

The Pythagorean Theorem

Glenda Lappan
James T. Fey
William M. Fitzgerald
Susan N. Friel
Elizabeth Difanis Phillips

PEARSON

Boston, Massachusetts · Glenview, Illinois · Shoreview, Minnesota · Upper Saddle River, New Jersey

Connected Mathematics™ was developed at Michigan State University with financial support from the Michigan State University Office of the Provost, Computing and Technology, and the College of Natural Science.

This material is based upon work supported by the National Science Foundation under Grant No. MDR 9150217 and Grant No. ESI 9986372. Opinions expressed are those of the authors and not necessarily those of the Foundation.

The Michigan State University authors and administration have agreed that all MSU royalties arising from this publication will be devoted to purposes supported by the Department of Mathematics and the MSU Mathematics Enrichment Fund.

13-digit ISBN 978-0-13-366202-3
10-digit ISBN 0-13-366202-0
2 3 4 5 6 7 8 9 10   11 10 09 08

Authors of Connected Mathematics

(from left to right) Glenda Lappan, Betty Phillips, Susan Friel, Bill Fitzgerald, Jim Fey

Glenda Lappan is a University Distinguished Professor in the Department of Mathematics at Michigan State University. Her research and development interests are in the connected areas of students' learning of mathematics and mathematics teachers' professional growth and change related to the development and enactment of K–12 curriculum materials.

James T. Fey is a Professor of Curriculum and Instruction and Mathematics at the University of Maryland. His consistent professional interest has been development and research focused on curriculum materials that engage middle and high school students in problem-based collaborative investigations of mathematical ideas and their applications.

William M. Fitzgerald (*Deceased*) was a Professor in the Department of Mathematics at Michigan State University. His early research was on the use of concrete materials in supporting student learning and led to the development of teaching materials for laboratory environments. Later he helped develop a teaching model to support student experimentation with mathematics.

Susan N. Friel is a Professor of Mathematics Education in the School of Education at the University of North Carolina at Chapel Hill. Her research interests focus on statistics education for middle-grade students and, more broadly, on teachers' professional development and growth in teaching mathematics K–8.

Elizabeth Difanis Phillips is a Senior Academic Specialist in the Mathematics Department of Michigan State University. She is interested in teaching and learning mathematics for both teachers and students. These interests have led to curriculum and professional development projects at the middle school and high school levels, as well as projects related to the teaching and learning of algebra across the grades.

CMP2 Development Staff

Teacher Collaborator in Residence
Yvonne Grant
Michigan State University

Production and Field Site Manager
Lisa Keller
Michigan State University

Administrative Assistant
Judith Martus Miller
Michigan State University

Technical and Editorial Support
**Brin Keller, Peter Lappan, Jim Laser,
Michael Masterson, Stacey Miceli**

Assessment Team
June Bailey and **Debra Sobko** (Apollo Middle School, Rochester, New York), **George Bright** (University of North Carolina, Greensboro), **Gwen Ranzau Campbell** (Sunrise Park Middle School, White Bear Lake, Minnesota), **Holly DeRosia, Kathy Dole,** and **Teri Keusch** (Portland Middle School, Portland, Michigan), **Mary Beth Schmitt** (Traverse City East Junior High School, Traverse City, Michigan), **Genni Steele** (Central Middle School, White Bear Lake, Minnesota), **Jacqueline Stewart** (Okemos, Michigan), **Elizabeth Tye** (Magnolia Junior High School, Magnolia, Arkansas)

Development Assistants
At Lansing Community College *Undergraduate Assistant:* **James Brinegar**

At Michigan State University *Graduate Assistants:* **Dawn Berk, Emily Bouck, Bulent Buyukbozkirli, Kuo-Liang Chang, Christopher Danielson, Srinivasa Dharmavaram, Deb Johanning, Wesley Kretzschmar, Kelly Rivette, Sarah Sword, Tat Ming Sze, Marie Turini, Jeffrey Wanko;** *Undergraduate Assistants:* **Daniel Briggs, Jeffrey Chapin, Jade Corsé, Elisha Hardy, Alisha Harold, Elizabeth Keusch, Julia Letoutchaia, Karen Loeffler, Brian Oliver, Carl Oliver, Evonne Pedawi, Lauren Rebrovich**

At the University of Maryland *Graduate Assistants:* **Kim Harris Bethea, Kara Karch**

At the University of North Carolina (Chapel Hill) *Graduate Assistants:* **Mark Ellis, Trista Stearns;** *Undergraduate Assistant:* **Daniel Smith**

Advisory Board for CMP2

Thomas Banchoff
Professor of Mathematics
Brown University
Providence, Rhode Island

Anne Bartel
Mathematics Coordinator
Minneapolis Public Schools
Minneapolis, Minnesota

Hyman Bass
Professor of Mathematics
University of Michigan
Ann Arbor, Michigan

Joan Ferrini-Mundy
Associate Dean of the College of
Natural Science; Professor
Michigan State University
East Lansing, Michigan

James Hiebert
Professor
University of Delaware
Newark, Delaware

Susan Hudson Hull
Charles A. Dana Center
University of Texas
Austin, Texas

Michele Luke
Mathematics Curriculum
Coordinator
West Junior High
Minnetonka, Minnesota

Kay McClain
Assistant Professor of
Mathematics Education
Vanderbilt University
Nashville, Tennessee

Edward Silver
Professor; Chair of Educational
Studies
University of Michigan
Ann Arbor, Michigan

Judith Sowder
Professor Emerita
San Diego State University
San Diego, California

Lisa Usher
Mathematics Resource Teacher
California Academy of
Mathematics and Science
San Pedro, California

Field Test Sites for CMP2

During the development of the revised edition of *Connected Mathematics* (CMP2), more than 100 classroom teachers have field-tested materials at 49 school sites in 12 states and the District of Columbia. This classroom testing occurred over three academic years (2001 through 2004), allowing careful study of the effectiveness of each of the 24 units that comprise the program. A special thanks to the students and teachers at these pilot schools.

Arkansas
Magnolia Public Schools
Kittena Bell*, Judith Trowell*; *Central Elementary School:* Maxine Broom, Betty Eddy, Tiffany Fallin, Bonnie Flurry, Carolyn Monk, Elizabeth Tye; *Magnolia Junior High School:* Monique Bryan, Ginger Cook, David Graham, Shelby Lamkin

Colorado
Boulder Public Schools
Nevin Platt Middle School: Judith Koenig

St. Vrain Valley School District, Longmont
Westview Middle School: Colleen Beyer, Kitty Canupp, Ellie Decker*, Peggy McCarthy, Tanya deNobrega, Cindy Payne, Ericka Pilon, Andrew Roberts

District of Columbia
Capitol Hill Day School: Ann Lawrence

Georgia
University of Georgia, Athens
Brad Findell
Madison Public Schools
Morgan County Middle School: Renee Burgdorf, Lynn Harris, Nancy Kurtz, Carolyn Stewart

Maine
Falmouth Public Schools
Falmouth Middle School: Donna Erikson, Joyce Hebert, Paula Hodgkins, Rick Hogan, David Legere, Cynthia Martin, Barbara Stiles, Shawn Towle*

Michigan
Portland Public Schools
Portland Middle School: Mark Braun, Holly DeRosia, Kathy Dole*, Angie Foote, Teri Keusch, Tammi Wardwell

Traverse City Area Public Schools
Bertha Vos Elementary: Kristin Sak; *Central Grade School:* Michelle Clark; Jody Meyers; *Eastern Elementary:* Karrie Tufts; *Interlochen Elementary:* Mary McGee-Cullen; *Long Lake Elementary:* Julie Faulkner*, Charlie Maxbauer, Katherine Sleder; *Norris Elementary:* Hope Slanaker; *Oak Park Elementary:* Jessica Steed; *Traverse Heights Elementary:* Jennifer Wolfert; *Westwoods Elementary:* Nancy Conn; *Old Mission Peninsula School:* Deb Larimer; *Traverse City East Junior High:* Ivanka Berkshire, Ruthanne Kladder, Jan Palkowski, Jane Peterson, Mary Beth Schmitt; *Traverse City West Junior High:* Dan Fouch*, Ray Fouch

Sturgis Public Schools
Sturgis Middle School: Ellen Eisele

Minnesota
Burnsville School District 191
Hidden Valley Elementary: Stephanie Cin, Jane McDevitt

Hopkins School District 270
Alice Smith Elementary: Sandra Cowing, Kathleen Gustafson, Martha Mason, Scott Stillman; *Eisenhower Elementary:* Chad Bellig, Patrick Berger, Nancy Glades, Kye Johnson, Shane Wasserman, Victoria Wilson; *Gatewood Elementary:* Sarah Ham, Julie Kloos, Janine Pung, Larry Wade; *Glen Lake Elementary:* Jacqueline Cramer, Kathy Hering, Cecelia Morris, Robb Trenda; *Katherine Curren Elementary:* Diane Bancroft, Sue DeWit, John Wilson; *L. H. Tanglen Elementary:* Kevin Athmann, Lisa Becker, Mary LaBelle, Kathy Rezac, Roberta Severson; *Meadowbrook Elementary:* Jan Gauger, Hildy Shank, Jessica Zimmerman; *North Junior High:* Laurel Hahn, Kristin Lee, Jodi Markuson, Bruce Mestemacher, Laurel Miller, Bonnie Rinker, Jeannine Salzer, Sarah Shafer, Cam Stottler; *West Junior High:* Alicia Beebe, Kristie Earl, Nobu Fujii, Pam Georgetti, Susan Gilbert, Regina Nelson Johnson, Debra Lindstrom, Michele Luke*, Jon Sorenson

Minneapolis School District 1
Ann Sullivan K–8 School: Bronwyn Collins; Anne Bartel* (Curriculum and Instruction Office)

Wayzata School District 284
Central Middle School: Sarajane Myers, Dan Nielsen, Tanya Ravnholdt

White Bear Lake School District 624
Central Middle School: Amy Jorgenson, Michelle Reich, Brenda Sammon

New York
New York City Public Schools
IS 89: Yelena Aynbinder, Chi-Man Ng, Nina Rapaport, Joel Spengler, Phyllis Tam*, Brent Wyso; *Wagner Middle School:* Jason Appel, Intissar Fernandez, Yee Gee Get, Richard Goldstein, Irving Marcus, Sue Norton, Bernadita Owens, Jennifer Rehn*, Kevin Yuhas

Ohio

Talawanda School District, Oxford
Talawanda Middle School: Teresa Abrams, Larry Brock, Heather Brosey, Julie Churchman, Monna Even, Karen Fitch, Bob George, Amanda Klee, Pat Meade, Sandy Montgomery, Barbara Sherman, Lauren Steidl

Miami University
Jeffrey Wanko*

Springfield Public Schools
Rockway School: Jim Mamer

Pennsylvania

Pittsburgh Public Schools
Kenneth Labuskes, Marianne O'Connor, Mary Lynn Raith*;
Arthur J. Rooney Middle School: David Hairston, Stamatina Mousetis, Alfredo Zangaro; *Frick International Studies Academy:* Suzanne Berry, Janet Falkowski, Constance Finseth, Romika Hodge, Frank Machi; *Reizenstein Middle School:* Jeff Baldwin, James Brautigam, Lorena Burnett, Glen Cobbett, Michael Jordan, Margaret Lazur, Tamar McPherson, Melissa Munnell, Holly Neely, Ingrid Reed, Dennis Reft

Texas

Austin Independent School District
Bedichek Middle School: Lisa Brown, Jennifer Glasscock, Vicki Massey

El Paso Independent School District
Cordova Middle School: Armando Aguirre, Anneliesa Durkes, Sylvia Guzman, Pat Holguin*, William Holguin, Nancy Nava, Laura Orozco, Michelle Peña, Roberta Rosen, Patsy Smith, Jeremy Wolf

Plano Independent School District
Patt Henry, James Wohlgehagen*; *Frankford Middle School:* Mandy Baker, Cheryl Butsch, Amy Dudley, Betsy Eshelman, Janet Greene, Cort Haynes, Kathy Letchworth, Kay Marshall, Kelly McCants, Amy Reck, Judy Scott, Syndy Snyder, Lisa Wang; *Wilson Middle School:* Darcie Bane, Amanda Bedenko, Whitney Evans, Tonelli Hatley, Sarah (Becky) Higgs, Kelly Johnston, Rebecca McElligott, Kay Neuse, Cheri Slocum, Kelli Straight

Washington

Evergreen School District
Shahala Middle School: Nicole Abrahamsen, Terry Coon*, Carey Doyle, Sheryl Drechsler, George Gemma, Gina Helland, Amy Hilario, Darla Lidyard, Sean McCarthy, Tilly Meyer, Willow Nuewelt, Todd Parsons, Brian Pederson, Stan Posey, Shawn Scott, Craig Sjoberg, Lynette Sundstrom, Charles Switzer, Luke Youngblood

Wisconsin

Beaver Dam Unified School District
Beaver Dam Middle School: Jim Braemer, Jeanne Frick, Jessica Greatens, Barbara Link, Dennis McCormick, Karen Michels, Nancy Nichols*, Nancy Palm, Shelly Stelsel, Susan Wiggins

---

* indicates a Field Test Site Coordinator

Reviews of CMP to Guide Development of CMP2

Before writing for CMP2 began or field tests were conducted, the first edition of *Connected Mathematics* was submitted to the mathematics faculties of school districts from many parts of the country and to 80 individual reviewers for extensive comments.

School District Survey Reviews of CMP

Arizona
Madison School District #38 (Phoenix)

Arkansas
Cabot School District, Little Rock School District, Magnolia School District

California
Los Angeles Unified School District

Colorado
St. Vrain Valley School District (Longmont)

Florida
Leon County Schools (Tallahassee)

Illinois
School District #21 (Wheeling)

Indiana
Joseph L. Block Junior High (East Chicago)

Kentucky
Fayette County Public Schools (Lexington)

Maine
Selection of Schools

Massachusetts
Selection of Schools

Michigan
Sparta Area Schools

Minnesota
Hopkins School District

Texas
Austin Independent School District, The El Paso Collaborative for Academic Excellence, Plano Independent School District

Wisconsin
Platteville Middle School

Individual Reviewers of CMP

Arkansas
Deborah Cramer; Robby Frizzell *(Taylor)*; Lowell Lynde *(University of Arkansas, Monticello)*; Leigh Manzer *(Norfork)*; Lynne Roberts *(Emerson High School, Emerson)*; Tony Timms *(Cabot Public Schools)*; Judith Trowell *(Arkansas Department of Higher Education)*

California
José Alcantar *(Gilroy)*; Eugenie Belcher *(Gilroy)*; Marian Pasternack *(Lowman M. S. T. Center, North Hollywood)*; Susana Pezoa *(San Jose)*; Todd Rabusin *(Hollister)*; Margaret Siegfried *(Ocala Middle School, San Jose)*; Polly Underwood *(Ocala Middle School, San Jose)*

Colorado
Janeane Golliher *(St. Vrain Valley School District, Longmont)*; Judith Koenig *(Nevin Platt Middle School, Boulder)*

Florida
Paige Loggins *(Swift Creek Middle School, Tallahassee)*

Illinois
Jan Robinson *(School District #21, Wheeling)*

Indiana
Frances Jackson *(Joseph L. Block Junior High, East Chicago)*

Kentucky
Natalee Feese *(Fayette County Public Schools, Lexington)*

Maine
Betsy Berry *(Maine Math & Science Alliance, Augusta)*

Maryland
Joseph Gagnon *(University of Maryland, College Park)*; Paula Maccini *(University of Maryland, College Park)*

Massachusetts
George Cobb *(Mt. Holyoke College, South Hadley)*; Cliff Kanold *(University of Massachusetts, Amherst)*

Michigan
Mary Bouck *(Farwell Area Schools)*; Carol Dorer *(Slauson Middle School, Ann Arbor)*; Carrie Heaney *(Forsythe Middle School, Ann Arbor)*; Ellen Hopkins *(Clague Middle School, Ann Arbor)*; Teri Keusch *(Portland Middle School, Portland)*; Valerie Mills *(Oakland Schools, Waterford)*; Mary Beth Schmitt *(Traverse City East Junior High, Traverse City)*; Jack Smith *(Michigan State University, East Lansing)*; Rebecca Spencer *(Sparta Middle School, Sparta)*; Ann Marie Nicoll Turner *(Tappan Middle School, Ann Arbor)*; Scott Turner *(Scarlett Middle School, Ann Arbor)*

Minnesota
Margarita Alvarez *(Olson Middle School, Minneapolis)*; Jane Amundson *(Nicollet Junior High, Burnsville)*; Anne Bartel *(Minneapolis Public Schools)*; Gwen Ranzau Campbell *(Sunrise Park Middle School, White Bear Lake)*; Stephanie Cin *(Hidden Valley Elementary, Burnsville)*; Joan Garfield *(University of Minnesota, Minneapolis)*; Gretchen Hall *(Richfield Middle School, Richfield)*; Jennifer Larson *(Olson Middle School, Minneapolis)*; Michele Luke *(West Junior High, Minnetonka)*; Jeni Meyer *(Richfield Junior High, Richfield)*; Judy Pfingsten *(Inver Grove Heights Middle School, Inver Grove Heights)*; Sarah Shafer *(North Junior High, Minnetonka)*; Genni Steele *(Central Middle School, White Bear Lake)*; Victoria Wilson *(Eisenhower Elementary, Hopkins)*; Paul Zorn *(St. Olaf College, Northfield)*

New York
Debra Altenau-Bartolino *(Greenwich Village Middle School, New York)*; Doug Clements *(University of Buffalo)*; Francis Curcio *(New York University, New York)*; Christine Dorosh *(Clinton School for Writers, Brooklyn)*; Jennifer Rehn *(East Side Middle School, New York)*; Phyllis Tam *(IS 89 Lab School, New York)*; Marie Turini *(Louis Armstrong Middle School, New York)*; Lucy West *(Community School District 2, New York)*; Monica Witt *(Simon Baruch Intermediate School 104, New York)*

Pennsylvania
Robert Aglietti *(Pittsburgh)*; Sharon Mihalich *(Freeport)*; Jennifer Plumb *(South Hills Middle School, Pittsburgh)*; Mary Lynn Raith *(Pittsburgh Public Schools)*

Texas
Michelle Bittick *(Austin Independent School District)*; Margaret Cregg *(Plano Independent School District)*; Sheila Cunningham *(Klein Independent School District)*; Judy Hill *(Austin Independent School District)*; Patricia Holguin *(El Paso Independent School District)*; Bonnie McNemar *(Arlington)*; Kay Neuse *(Plano Independent School District)*; Joyce Polanco *(Austin Independent School District)*; Marge Ramirez *(University of Texas at El Paso)*; Pat Rossman *(Baker Campus, Austin)*; Cindy Schimek *(Houston)*; Cynthia Schneider *(Charles A. Dana Center, University of Texas at Austin)*; Uri Treisman *(Charles A. Dana Center, University of Texas at Austin)*; Jacqueline Weilmuenster *(Grapevine-Colleyville Independent School District)*; LuAnn Weynand *(San Antonio)*; Carmen Whitman *(Austin Independent School District)*; James Wohlgehagen *(Plano Independent School District)*

Washington
Ramesh Gangolli *(University of Washington, Seattle)*

Wisconsin
Susan Lamon *(Marquette University, Hales Corner)*; Steve Reinhart *(retired, Chippewa Falls Middle School, Eau Claire)*

Table of Contents

Looking For Pythagoras
The Pythagorean Theorem

The Student Edition pages for the Unit Opener follow page 14.

Unit Introduction

Looking for Pythagoras
The Pythagorean Theorem

Goals of the Unit

- Relate the area of a square to the side length

- Estimate the values of square roots of whole numbers

- Locate irrational numbers on a number line

- Develop strategies for finding the distance between two points on a coordinate grid

- Understand and apply the Pythagorean Theorem

- Use the Pythagorean Theorem to solve everyday problems

Developing Students' Mathematical Habits

The overall goal of *Connected Mathematics* is to help students develop sound mathematical habits. Through their work in this and other geometry units, students learn important questions to ask themselves about any situation that can be represented and modeled mathematically, such as

- *Is it appropriate and useful to use the Pythagorean Theorem in this situation? How do I know this?*

- *Do I need to find the distance between two points?*

- *What are the quantities in this problem?*

- *How can I estimate the square root of a number?*

- *How can I find the length of something without directly measuring it?*

Overview

In *Looking for Pythagoras*, students explore two important ideas: the Pythagorean Theorem and square roots. They also review and make connections among the concepts of area, distance, and irrational numbers.

Students begin the unit by finding the distance between points on a coordinate grid. They learn that the positive square root of a number is the side length of a square whose area is that number. Then, students discover the Pythagorean relationship through an exploration of squares drawn on the sides of a right triangle. In the last investigation of the unit, students apply the Pythagorean Theorem to a variety of problems.

Summary of Investigations

Investigation 1
Coordinate Grids

Students review coordinate grids as they analyze a map in which streets are laid out on a grid. They make the connection between the coordinates of two points and the driving distance between them. This sets the stage for finding the distance between two points on a grid without measuring. Students investigate geometric figures on coordinate grids. Given two vertices, they find other vertices that define a square, a non-square rectangle, a right triangle, and a non-rectangular parallelogram. And, they calculate areas of several figures drawn on a dot grid.

Investigation 2
Squaring Off

Students explore the relationship between the area of a square drawn on a dot grid and the length of its sides. This provides an introduction to the concept of square root. They find the distance between two points by analyzing the line segment between them: they draw a square using the segment as one side, find the area of the square, and then find the positive square root of that area.

Investigation 3
The Pythagorean Theorem

Students develop and explore the Pythagorean Theorem. They then investigate a geometric puzzle that verifies the theorem, and they use the theorem to find the distance between two points on a grid. In the last problem, they explore and apply the converse of the Pythagorean Theorem.

Investigation 4
Using the Pythagorean Theorem

For students to appreciate the mathematical power of the Pythagorean Theorem, they need to encounter situations that can be illuminated by the theorem. Students explore an interesting pattern among right triangles, apply the Pythagorean Theorem to find distances on a baseball diamond, investigate properties of 30-60-90 triangles, and find missing lengths and angle measures of a triangle composed of smaller triangles.

Mathematics Background

Students' work in this unit develops an important relationship connecting geometry and algebra: the Pythagorean Theorem. The presentation of ideas reflects the historical development of the concept of irrational numbers. Early Greek mathematicians searched for ratios of integers to represent side lengths of squares with certain given areas such as 2 square units. The square root of 2 is an irrational number, which means that it cannot be written as a ratio of two integers.

Finding Area and Distance

Students find areas of plane figures drawn on dot grids. This reviews some concepts developed in the grade 6 unit *Covering and Surrounding*. One common method for calculating the area of a figure is to subdivide it and add the areas of the component shapes. A second common method is to enclose the shape in a rectangle and subtract the areas of the shapes that lie outside the figure from the area of the rectangle. Below, the area of the shape is found with each method.

Subdivide to find the area:
$$2 + 2 + 1 + 1 = 6$$

Enclose in a square to find the area:
$$16 - (4 + 2 + 2\tfrac{1}{2} + 1\tfrac{1}{2}) = 6$$

In Investigation 2, students draw squares with as many different areas as possible on a 5 dot-by-5 dot grid. There are eight possible squares, four "upright" and four "tilted."

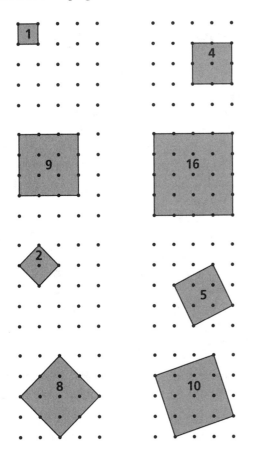

Square Roots

If the area of a square is known, its side length is easy to determine: it is the number whose square is the area. The fact that some of these lengths are not whole numbers prompts the introduction of the $\sqrt{}$ symbol. The lengths of the sides of the preceding squares (in units) are 1, 2, 3, 4, $\sqrt{2}$, $\sqrt{5}$, $\sqrt{8}$, and $\sqrt{10}$. Because the grid is a centimeter grid, students can estimate the values of the square roots by measuring these lengths with a ruler. By making these ruler estimates and comparing them to estimates obtained by computing square roots on a calculator, students develop a sense of these numbers and begin to realize that they cannot be expressed as terminating or repeating decimals.

Students also develop benchmarks for estimating square roots. For example, $\sqrt{5}$ is between 2 and 3 because $4 < 5 < 9$, and since 5 is closer to 4 than 9, we estimate that $\sqrt{5}$ is closer to 2 than 3. Students might try 2.25. But $2.25^2 = 5.06$. So, $\sqrt{5}$ is between 2 and 2.25, but closer to 2.25. They might try 2.24 to get $2.24^2 = 5.0176$, which is closer. This method can be continued until the desired accuracy is obtained. Students also estimate square roots with a number line ruler, which helps them to develop a sense of the size of the irrational numbers such as $\sqrt{3}$, $\sqrt{5}$, and $\sqrt{7}$. One way to locate $\sqrt{2}$ on the number line is as follows:

The square below has an area of 2 square units. The length of a side of this square is $\sqrt{2}$ units. If we draw a number line as shown, and use a compass to mark off a segment with the same length as a side of the square, we can see that the segment is about 1.4 units long.

Using Squares to Find Lengths of Segments

Finding the areas of squares leads students to a method for finding the distance between two dots. The distance between two dots on a dot grid is the length of the line segment connecting them. To find this length, students can draw a square with the segment as one side. The distance between the two dots is the square root of the area of the square.

To use this method to find all the different lengths of line segments that can be drawn on a 5 dot-by-5 dot grid, the grid must be extended to fit the squares associated with those lengths. For example, the bold line segment below is the side of a square (shaded) with an area of 25 square units, so the segment has length $\sqrt{25}$ units, or 5 units.

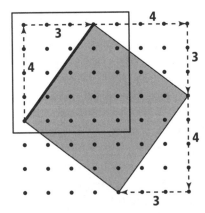

To draw the square with the given side length, many students will use an "up and over" or "down and over" method to go from one point to the next. For example, to get from the lower endpoint of the segment above to the other endpoint, you go up 4 units and right 3 units. These endpoints are two vertices of the square. To get the third vertex, go right 4 units and down 3. To get the fourth, go down 4 units and to the left 3. In this way, they are developing intuition about the Pythagorean Theorem.

Developing and Using the Pythagorean Theorem

Once students are comfortable with finding the length of a segment by thinking of it as the side of a square, they investigate the patterns among the areas of the three squares that can be drawn on the sides of a right triangle.

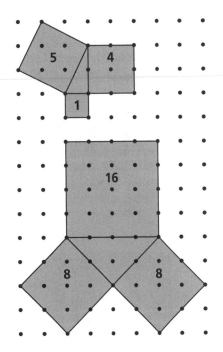

The observation that the square on the hypotenuse has an area equal to the sum of the areas of the squares on the legs leads students to the Pythagorean Theorem: If a and b are the lengths of the legs of a right triangle and c is the length of the hypotenuse, then $a^2 + b^2 = c^2$.

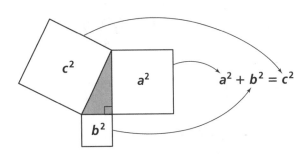

A *theorem* is a general mathematical statement that has been proven true. Over 300 different proofs have been given for the Pythagorean Theorem. It is regarded as one of the most important developments in mathematics because it allows us to link ideas of number to ideas of space.

A Proof of the Pythagorean Theorem

Students solve a puzzle that gives a geometric proof of the Pythagorean Theorem. The puzzle pieces consist of eight congruent right triangles and three squares.

Puzzle frames   **Puzzle pieces**

The side lengths of the squares are the lengths of the three triangle sides.

To solve the puzzle, students must arrange the pieces to fit into two square puzzle frames. Students' arrangements of the 11 shapes may differ slightly, but all arrangements lead to the same conclusion.

One possible arrangement is shown below. The sides' lengths of the right triangle have been labeled a, b, and c.

Once the shapes are arranged, you can reason as follows:

- The areas of the frames are equal. They are squares with side lengths of $a + b$.

- Each frame contains four identical right triangles. The other shapes are squares with area a^2, b^2, and c^2.

- If the four right triangles are removed from each frame, the area remaining in the two frames must be equal. That is, the sum of the areas of the squares in one frame must equal the area of the square in the other frame.

Geometrically, the diagram shows that if the lengths of the legs of a right triangle are a and b, and the length of the hypotenuse is c, then $a^2 + b^2 = c^2$. You can make similar puzzle pieces starting with any right triangle and then arrange the shapes in the same way. Therefore, this statement is true for any right triangle.

In later courses, students may see this geometric argument presented algebraically. The sum of the areas of the two squares and the four triangles in the left frame equals the sum of the areas of the square and the four triangles in the right frame:

$$a^2 + b^2 + 4\left(\frac{ab}{2}\right) = c^2 + 4\left(\frac{ab}{2}\right)$$
$$a^2 + b^2 = c^2$$

The Pythagorean Theorem has many applications that connect the concepts of line segment lengths, squares, and right angles.

Using the Pythagorean Theorem to Find Lengths

Students use the Pythagorean Theorem to find the distance between two dots on a dot grid. The length of a horizontal or vertical line segment drawn on a dot grid can be found by counting the units directly. If the segment is not vertical or horizontal, it is always possible to treat it as the hypotenuse of a right triangle with vertical and horizontal legs. The length of the hypotenuse—and thus the distance between the dots—can then be found with the Pythagorean Theorem.

In high school, students will see the following formula for finding the distance between two points, (x_1, y_1) and (x_2, y_2) in the plane:

$$d = \sqrt{(x_1 - x_2)^2 + (y_1 - y_2)^2}$$

This is simply the Pythagorean Theorem where $a = x_1 - x_2$ (the horizontal distance between two points), $b = y_1 - y_2$ (the vertical distance between two points), and $c = d$.

To find the length of line segment AB below, draw a right triangle with segment AB as the hypotenuse. Calculate the areas of the squares on the legs of the triangle (4 square units each), add these areas (8 square units, which is the area of the square drawn on the hypotenuse), and take the square root. The length of AB is $\sqrt{8}$ units.

The Converse of the Pythagorean Theorem

The *converse* of a statement of the form "If p then q" is "If q then p." The converse of the Pythagorean Theorem states: If a, b, and c are the lengths of the sides of a triangle and $a^2 + b^2 = c^2$, then the triangle is a right triangle. The converse of a true statement is not always true. However, the converse of the Pythagorean Theorem is true and can be used to show that a given triangle is a right triangle. For example, if you know the side lengths of a triangle are 6 in., 8 in., and 10 in., then because $6^2 + 8^2 = 10^2$, you can conclude that the triangle is a right triangle.

Students do not formally prove the converse of the Pythagorean Theorem in this unit. Rather, they build triangles with a variety of different side lengths and determine whether they are right triangles. Based on their findings, they conjecture that triangles whose side lengths satisfy $a^2 + b^2 = c^2$ are right triangles.

Students are asked to explain why their conjecture is true. One explanation is: "Suppose we know that Triangle 1 has sides a, b, and c, that satisfy the relationship $a^2 + b^2 = c^2$. Suppose Triangle 2 has sides a, b, and d and we know that Triangle 2 is a right triangle with leg lengths of a and b. Then $a^2 + b^2 = d^2$. From the first statement we know that $a^2 + b^2 = c^2$. Logically, this gives us that $c^2 = d^2$, and, therefore, $c = d$ (because they must both be positive numbers). Now Triangle 1 and Triangle 2 have the same three measures for their sides. In *Shapes and Designs*, students learned that once you know all three sides of a triangle, it is uniquely identified. They will investigate this idea more formally when they study congruence of triangles in *Hubcaps, Kaleidoscopes, and Mirrors*. So these two triangles are identical, right-angled triangles. In other words it is impossible for a triangle whose sides fit the relationship $a^2 + b^2 = c^2$ to not be a right-angled triangle.

An interesting byproduct of the converse of the Pythagorean Theorem is the concept of *Pythagorean triples*, sets of numbers that satisfy the relationship $a^2 + b^2 = c^2$. Students discover that finding Pythagorean triples means finding two square numbers whose sum is also a square number. Multiples of one triple will generate countless others. For example, once you establish that 3-4-5 is a Pythagorean triple, you know that 6-8-10, 9-12-15, and so on, are also Pythagorean triples.

Special Right Triangles

In Investigation 4, students learn about 30-60-90 triangles by starting with an equilateral triangle (a 60-60-60 triangle). They use the line of symmetry to show the reflection line forms two congruent 30-60-90 triangles. For each of these triangles, they deduce that the leg opposite the 30° angle is half the length of the side of the original triangle. They then use the Pythagorean Theorem to find the length of the other leg.

The Pythagorean Theorem can be used to show some special relationships among side lengths of 30-60-90 triangles (that is, triangles with 30°, 60°, and 90° angles).

Suppose the hypotenuse of a 30-60-90 triangle has length c. The length of the side opposite the 30° angle must be half this length, or $\frac{c}{2}$. Using the Pythagorean Theorem, the square of the length of the longer leg is $c^2 - \frac{c^2}{4}$, or $\frac{3c^2}{4}$. So, its length is $\sqrt{\frac{3c^2}{4}}$, or $\frac{c\sqrt{3}}{2}$.

Students also explore isosceles right triangles (45-45-90 triangles), and find that the length of the hypotenuse is always the length of one of the legs times $\sqrt{2}$. If the length of each leg is a then, by the Pythagorean Theorem, the square of the length of the hypotenuse must be $a^2 + a^2$, or $2a^2$. Therefore, the length of the hypotenuse is $\sqrt{2a^2} = a\sqrt{2}$.

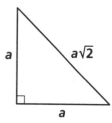

Rational and Irrational Numbers

When we examine patterns in the decimal representations of fractions, or rational numbers, we find that the decimals either terminate or repeat. For example, $\frac{1}{5}$ is equal to 0.2 (a terminating decimal) and $\frac{1}{3}$ is equal to 0.33333... (a repeating decimal). Numbers such as $\sqrt{2}$, $\sqrt{3}$, and $\sqrt{5}$ cannot be expressed as repeating or terminating decimals. Students create line segments with these lengths. For example, $\sqrt{2}$ is the length of the hypotenuse of a right triangle whose legs have length 1. They then locate the lengths on a number line. This procedure helps students to estimate the size of these irrational numbers.

Converting Repeating Decimals to Fractions

Because all repeating decimals are rational numbers, they can be represented as fractions. It is not always obvious, though, what fraction is equivalent to a given repeating decimal. One method for converting a repeating decimal to a

fraction involves solving an equation. To convert 12.312312... to a fraction, for example, call the unknown fraction N. Thus, $N = 12.312312....$ Multiply both sides of the equation by 1,000 (the power of 10 that moves a complete repeating group to the left of the decimal point), which gives $1,000N = 12,312.312312....$ Then, subtract the first equation from the second, which gives $999N = 12,300$. Therefore, $N = \frac{12,300}{999}$, or $12\frac{312}{999}$.

The decimal equivalents of fractions with denominators of 9, 99, 999, and so on, display interesting patterns that can be used to write repeating decimals as fractions. For example, all decimals with a repeating part of one digit, such as 0.111... and 0.222..., can be written as a fraction with 9 in the denominator and the repeated digit in the numerator, such as $\frac{1}{9}$ and $\frac{2}{9}$. Decimals with a repeating part of two digits, such as 0.010101... and 0.121212..., can be written as a fraction with 99 in the denominator and the repeated digits in the numerator, such as $\frac{1}{99}$ and $\frac{12}{99}$.

Proof that $\sqrt{2}$ Is Irrational

In high school, students may prove that $\sqrt{2}$ is not a rational number. Its irrationality can be proved in an interesting way—a proof by contradiction. The proof is given here for the teacher's information.

Assume $\sqrt{2}$ is rational. Then, there exist positive integers p and q such that $\sqrt{2} = \frac{p}{q}$. So, $\sqrt{2}q = p$. Squaring both sides gives $2q^2 = p^2$. From the *Prime Time* unit students learned that all square numbers have an odd number of factors. The reason is that factors of a number come in pairs. In a square number the factors in one of the pairs must be equal, which makes the number of factors for a square number odd. This means that if p and q are positive integers, then p^2 and q^2 each have an odd number of factors. Since $p^2 = 2q^2$, p^2 has the same number of factors as $2q^2$. But $2q^2$ has an even number of factors (The factor 2 plus the odd number of factors of q^2.) This is a contradiction. Therefore, p and q cannot exist with these properties and $\sqrt{2}$ must be irrational.

Square Root Versus Decimal Approximation

Problems involving the Pythagorean Theorem often result in square roots that are irrational numbers. Students at this level are often reluctant to leave numbers in a square root form. For example, rather than give an exact answer of $\sqrt{3}$, they give a decimal approximation, such as 1.732. Some students are not comfortable thinking about square roots as numbers. Although it is important to know the approximate size of an answer, especially in a practical problem, it is sometimes better to give an exact answer, and this often means using square root form. For example, in the study of 30-60-90 triangles,

$$\frac{\text{length of leg opposite the 60° angle}}{\text{length of the hypotenuse}} = \frac{\sqrt{3}}{2}$$

Here, $\sqrt{3}$ is much easier to remember than a multi-digit decimal approximation, and the expression using the square root gives the exact result. Similarly, in a right triangle, if the hypotenuse has a length of 9 units and one leg has a length of 8 units, then the length of the other leg is $\sqrt{81 - 64} = \sqrt{17}$ units. This answer is exact, while the calculator answer, 4.123105626, is an approximation. This is not to say that all answers should be left in square root form—context needs to be considered. Heights of buildings are more easily comprehended in whole-number or decimal form, even if that form does not give the precise answer. Students should be encouraged to leave an answer in square root form when there is no practical reason to express it as a decimal approximation. The hope is that all students will become comfortable with square roots as numbers in contexts where expressing an answer as a square root is appropriate. In this unit, we want students to have a "sense" of square roots as numbers and some idea of where they fit on the number line or between what two rational numbers they occur.

Number Systems

New number systems are created when a problem arises that cannot be answered within the system currently in use, or when inconsistencies arise that can be taken care of only by expanding the domain of numbers in the system.

The historical "discoveries" of new number systems in response to needs are reflected in the number sets students use in grades K–12. Elementary students begin with the *counting numbers*, also called *natural numbers*. Then, zero is added to the system to create the set of *whole numbers*. Later, students learn that negative numbers are needed to give meaning in certain contexts, such as temperature. Now they have the number system called the *integers*.

In elementary and middle school, students learn about fractions and situations in which fractions are useful, as in many division problems. Students' number world has been expanded to the set of *rational numbers*.

In this unit, students encounter contexts in which the need for *irrational numbers* arises. Specifically, they need irrational numbers to express the exact lengths of tilted segments on a grid. The set of rational numbers and the set of irrational numbers compose the set of *real numbers*. The diagram in Figure 1 is one way to represent these sets of numbers.

Figure 1

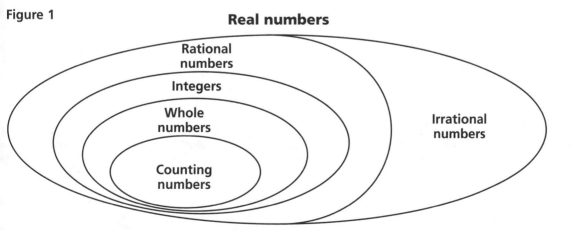

Real numbers
Rational numbers
Integers
Whole numbers
Counting numbers
Irrational numbers

Big Idea	Prior Work	Future Work
Calculating the distance between two points in the plane	Measuring lengths (*Shapes and Designs; Covering and Surrounding*); working with coordinates (*Variables and Patterns; Moving Straight Ahead; Thinking With Mathematical Models*)	Finding midpoints of line segments (*Kaleidoscopes, Hubcaps, and Mirrors*)
Finding areas of figures drawn on a coordinate grid with whole-number vertices	Measuring areas of polygons and irregular figures (*Bits and Pieces I; Covering and Surrounding*) and surface areas of three-dimensional shapes (*Filling and Wrapping*)	Studying transformations and symmetries of plane figures (*Kaleidoscopes, Hubcaps, and Mirrors*)
Understanding square roots as lengths of sides of squares	Applying the formula for area of a square (*Covering and Surrounding*)	Looking for patterns in square numbers (*Frogs, Fleas, and Painted Cubes*); looking for patterns in exponents (*Growing, Growing, Growing*)
Understanding the Pythagorean Theorem and how it relates the areas of the squares on the sides of a right triangle	Formulating, reading, and interpreting symbolic rules (*Variables and Patterns; Moving Straight Ahead; Thinking With Mathematical Models; Covering and Surrounding*); working with the triangle inequality (*Shapes and Designs*)	Formulating and using symbolic rules and the syntax for manipulating symbols (*Frogs, Fleas, and Painted Cubes; Say It With Symbols; Shapes of Algebra*)
Using the Pythagorean Theorem to solve problems	Solving problems in geometric and algebraic contexts (*Shapes and Designs; Moving Straight Ahead; Thinking With Mathematical Models; Covering and Surrounding*)	Solving geometric and algebraic problems (*Growing, Growing, Growing; Frogs, Fleas, and Painted Cubes; Say It With Symbols; Kaleidoscopes, Hubcaps, and Mirrors*)
Investigating rational numbers written as decimals	Understanding fractions and decimals (*Bits and Pieces I, II, and III*)	Exploring sampling and approximations (*Growing, Growing, Growing; Samples and Populations; Frogs, Fleas, and Painted Cubes*)
Understanding irrational numbers as non-terminating, non-repeating decimals	Representing fractions as decimals and decimals as fractions (*Bits and Pieces I, II, and III*)	Solving quadratic equations (*Growing, Growing, Growing; Frogs, Fleas, and Painted Cubes; Say It With Symbols*)
Understanding slope relationships of perpendicular and parallel lines	Finding slopes of lines and investigating parallel lines (*Variables and Patterns; Moving Straight Ahead*)	Investigating symmetry (*Kaleidoscopes, Hubcaps, and Mirrors*); finding the equation of a circle (*Shapes of Algebra*)

Planning for the Unit

Pacing Suggestions and Materials

Investigations and Assessments	Pacing 45–50 min. classes	Materials for Students	Materials for Teachers
1 Coordinate Grids	$3\frac{1}{2}$ days	Labsheets 1.1–1.3, dot paper (optional), geoboards (optional), Labsheet 1ACE Exercises 15–25	Transparencies 1.1A, 1.1B, 1.2A, 1.2B, and 1.3
Mathematical Reflections	$\frac{1}{2}$ day		
2 Squaring Off	$3\frac{1}{2}$ days	Labsheets 2.1 and 2.3, geoboards (optional)	Transparencies 2.1, 2.2, and 2.3A–C
Mathematical Reflections	$\frac{1}{2}$ day		
Assessment: Check Up	1 day		
3 The Pythagorean Theorem	$5\frac{1}{2}$ days	Labsheets 3.2A–C and 3.3; scissors; string; straws or polystrips (optional); markers, tape; angle ruler or protractor	Transparencies 3.1, 3.2A, 3.2B, 3.3, and 3.4
Mathematical Reflections	$\frac{1}{2}$ day		
Assessment: Partner Quiz	1 day		
4 Using the Pythagorean Theorem	$4\frac{1}{2}$ days	Labsheets 4.1 and 4.4, dot paper, scissors	Transparencies 4.1A, 4.1B, 4.2, 4.3A, 4.3B, and 4.4
Mathematical Reflections	$\frac{1}{2}$ day		
Looking Back and Looking Ahead	$\frac{1}{2}$ day		
Assessment: Self Assessment	Take Home		
Assessment: Unit Test	1 day		

Total Time	$22\frac{1}{2}$ **days**	**Materials for Use in All Investigations**	
For detailed pacing for Problems within each Investigation, see the Suggested Pacing at the beginning of each Investigation.		Calculators, centimeter rulers, student notebooks	Blank transparencies and transparency markers (optional)
For pacing with block scheduling, see next page.			

Pacing for Block Scheduling (90-minute class periods)

Investigation	Suggested Pacing	Investigation	Suggested Pacing
Investigation 1	$2\frac{1}{2}$ days	**Investigation 3**	$3\frac{1}{2}$ days
Problem 1.1	1 day	Problem 3.1	1 day
Problem 1.2	$\frac{1}{2}$ day	Problem 3.2	$\frac{1}{2}$ day
Problem 1.3	$\frac{1}{2}$ day	Problem 3.3	$\frac{1}{2}$ day
Math Reflections	$\frac{1}{2}$ day	Problem 3.4	1 day
Investigation 2	$2\frac{1}{2}$ days	Math Reflections	$\frac{1}{2}$ day
Problem 2.1	$\frac{1}{2}$ day	**Investigation 4**	**3 days**
Problem 2.2	1 day	Problem 4.1	$\frac{1}{2}$ day
Problem 2.3	$\frac{1}{2}$ day	Problem 4.2	$\frac{1}{2}$ day
Math Reflections	$\frac{1}{2}$ day	Problem 4.3	1 day
		Problem 4.4	$\frac{1}{2}$ day
		Math Reflections	$\frac{1}{2}$ day

Vocabulary

Essential Terms Developed in This Unit	Useful Terms Referenced in This Unit	Terms Developed in Previous Units	
hypotenuse	conjecture	area	perimeter
legs	irrational number	congruent	perpendicular lines
Pythagorean Theorem	isosceles triangle	coordinate grid	quadrilateral
real numbers	rational number	coordinates	ratio
square root	repeating decimal	equilateral triangle	right angle
	terminating decimal	length	right triangle
	30-60-90 right triangle	parallel lines	square
		parallelogram	symmetry

Program Resources

Go Online
PHSchool.com
For: Teacher Resources
Web Code: apk–5500

Components

Use the chart below to quickly see which components are available for each Investigation.

Invest.	Labsheets	Additional Practice	Transparencies		Formal Assessment		Assessment Options	
			Problem	Summary	Check Up	Partner Quiz	Multiple-Choice	Question Bank
1	1.1, 1.2, 1.3, 1ACE Exercises 15–25	✔	1.1A, 1.1B, 1.2A, 1.2B, 1.3					✔
2	2.1, 2.3	✔	2.1, 2.2, 2.3A, 2.3B		✔		✔	✔
3	3.2A–C, 3.3	✔	3.1, 3.2A, 3.2B, 3.3, 3.4			✔	✔	✔
4	4.1, 4.4, Dot Paper	✔	4.1A, 4.1B, 4.2, 4.3A, 4.3B, 4.4				✔	✔
For the Unit		*ExamView* CD-ROM, Web site	LBLA		Unit Test, Notebook Check, Self Assessment		Multiple-Choice Items, Question Bank, *ExamView* CD-ROM	

Also Available for Use With This Unit

- Parent Guide: take-home letter for the unit
- Implementing CMP
- Spanish Assessment Resources
- Additional online and technology resources

Technology

The Use of Calculators

Connected Mathematics was developed with the belief that calculators should be available and that students should learn when their use is appropriate. For this reason, we do not designate specific problems as "calculator problems." However, students will need access to graphing calculators for much of their work in this unit. Occasionally, students will be asked not to use their calculators to encourage them to think about how they can estimate square roots.

Student Interactivity CD-ROM

Includes interactive activities to enhance the learning in the Problems within Investigations.

PHSchool.com

For Students Multiple-choice practice with instant feedback, updated data sources, data sets for Tinkerplots data software.

For Teachers Professional development, curriculum support, downloadable forms, and more.

See also www.math.msu.edu/cmp for more resources for both teachers and students.

ExamView® CD-ROM

Create multiple versions of practice sheets and tests for course objectives and standardized tests. Includes dynamic questions, online testing, student reports, and all test and practice items in Spanish. Also includes all items in the *Assessment Resources* and *Additional Practice*.

TeacherExpress™ CD-ROM

Includes a lesson planning tool, the Teacher's Guide pages, and all the teaching resources.

LessonLab Online Courses

LessonLab offers comprehensive, facilitated, professional development designed to help teachers implement CMP2 and improve student achievement. To learn more, please visit PHSchool.com/cmp2.

Ongoing Informal Assessment

Embedded in the Student Unit

Problems Use students' work from the Problems to check student understanding.

ACE exercises Use ACE exercises for homework assignments to assess student understanding.

Mathematical Reflections Have students summarize their learning at the end of each Investigation.

Looking Back and Looking Ahead At the end of the unit, use the first two sections to allow students to show what they know about the unit.

Additional Resources

Teacher's Guide Use the Check for Understanding feature of some Summaries and the probing questions that appear in the *Launch, Explore,* or *Summarize* sections of all Investigations to check student understanding.

Summary Transparencies Use these transparencies to focus class attention on a summary check for understanding.

Self Assessment

Notebook Check Students use this tool to organize and check their notebooks before giving them to their teacher. Located in *Assessment Resources.*

Self Assessment At the end of the unit, students reflect on and provide examples of what they learned. Located in *Assessment Resources.*

Formal Assessment

Choose the assessment materials that are appropriate for your students.

Assessment	For Use After	Focus	Student Work
Check Up	Invest. 2	Skills	Individual
Partner Quiz	Invest. 3	Rich problems	Group
Unit Test	The Unit	Skills, rich problems	Individual

Additional Resources

Multiple-Choice Items Use these items for homework, review, a quiz, or add them to the Unit Test.

Question Bank Choose from these questions for homework, review, or replacements for Quiz, Check Up, or Unit Test questions.

Additional Practice Choose practice exercises for each investigation for homework, review, or formal assessments.

ExamView **CD-ROM** Create practice sheets, review quizzes, and tests with this dynamic software. Give online tests and receive student progress reports. (All test items available in Spanish.)

Spanish Assessment Resources

Includes Partner Quizzes, Check Ups, Unit Test, Multiple-Choice Items, Question Bank, Notebook Check, and Self Assessment. Plus, the *ExamView* CD-ROM has all test items in Spanish.

Correlation to Standardized Tests

Investigation	NAEP	Terra Nova CAT6	CTBS	ITBS	SAT10	Local Test
1 Coordinate Grids	A2c					
2 Squaring Off	N2d		✔		✔	
3 The Pythagorean Theorem	G3d					
4 Using the Pythagorean Theorem	G3d					

NAEP National Assessment of Educational Progress   **CAT6/Terra Nova** California Achievement Test, 6th Ed.   **CTBS/Terra Nova** Comprehensive Test of Basic Skills   **ITBS** Iowa Test of Basic Skills, Form M   **SAT10** Stanford Achievement Test, 1

Connected Mathematics 2™

Looking for Pythagoras

The Pythagorean Theorem

Glenda Lappan

James T. Fey

William M. Fitzgerald

Susan N. Friel

Elizabeth Difanis Phillips

PEARSON

Boston, Massachusetts · Glenview, Illinois · Shoreview, Minnesota · Upper Saddle River, New Jersey

Notes

Looking for Pythagoras

The Pythagorean Theorem

Suppose you are planning an airplane trip to several cities in your state. What types of information would you need to give the pilot so he would know where to go?

To mark the square corners of their property, ancient Egyptians used a rope divided by knots into 12 equal segments. How do you think they used this tool?

On a standard baseball diamond, the bases are 90 feet apart. How far must a catcher at home plate throw the ball to get a runner out at second base?

2 Looking for Pythagoras

Notes _____

_____

_____

_____

In this unit, you will explore side lengths and areas of right triangles and squares. Your explorations will lead you to discover one of the most important relationships in all of mathematics: the *Pythagorean Theorem*. The Pythagorean Theorem is so important that much of geometry, trigonometry, and calculus would be impossible without it.

In your previous work, you used whole numbers and fractions to describe lengths. In this unit, you will work with lengths that are impossible to describe with whole numbers or fractions. To talk about such lengths, you need to use another type of number, called an *irrational number*.

As you work on this unit, you will use what you are learning to solve problems like those on the previous page.

Notes

Mathematical Highlights

The Pythagorean Theorem

In *Looking for Pythagoras,* you will explore an important relationship among the side lengths of a right triangle.

You will learn how to

- Relate the area of a square to its side length
- Develop strategies for finding the distance between two points on a coordinate grid
- Understand and apply the Pythagorean Theorem
- Estimate the values of square roots of whole numbers
- Use the Pythagorean Theorem to solve everyday problems
- Locate irrational numbers on a number line

As you work on problems in this unit, ask yourself questions about problem situations that involve right triangles:

Is it appropriate and useful to use the Pythagorean Theorem in this situation? How do I know this?

Do I need to find the distance between two points?

How are irrational numbers and areas of squares related?

How can I estimate the square root of a number?

How can I find the length of something without directly measuring it?

Notes _____

_____

_____

Introducing Your Students to *Looking for Pythagoras*

One way to introduce *Looking for Pythagoras* is to ask your students to brainstorm about the ways they can measure something they cannot reach. They should remember some principles of indirect measurement from their work in the grade 7 unit *Stretching and Shrinking*. Tell your students that, in *Looking for Pythagoras*, they will study right triangles, distances, and indirect measurement.

Using the Unit Opener

Discuss the questions posed on the opening page of the Student Edition, which are designed to start students thinking about the kinds of questions and mathematics in the unit. Don't look for "correct" answers at this time. Do, however, present an opportunity for the class to discuss the questions and to start to think about what is needed to answer them. You may want to revisit these questions as students learn the mathematical ideas and techniques necessary to find the answers.

Problems in contexts are used to help students informally reason about the mathematics of the unit. The problems are deliberately sequenced to develop understanding of concepts and skills.

Using the Mathematical Highlights

The Mathematical Highlights page in the student edition provides information to students, parents, and other family members. It gives students a preview of the mathematics and some of the overarching questions that they should ask themselves while studying *Looking for Pythagoras*.

As they work through the unit, students can refer back to the Mathematical Highlights page to review what they have learned and to preview what is still to come. This page also tells students' families what mathematical ideas and activities will be covered as the class works through *Looking for Pythagoras*.

Investigation 1 · Coordinate Grids

Mathematical and Problem-Solving Goals

- Review the coordinate system
- Explore distances on a coordinate grid
- Review properties of quadrilaterals
- Connect properties of figures to coordinate representations
- Draw shapes on a coordinate grid
- Develop strategies for finding areas of irregular figures on a grid

Summary of Problems

Problem 1.1 Driving Around Euclid

Students analyze a map of a fictitious city in which streets are laid out on a coordinate grid. They find driving distances from one location to another, making the connection between the coordinates of two points and the distance between them. They compare the driving and flying distances between two points.

Problem 1.2 Planning Parks

Given two vertices, students find other vertices that define a square, a non-square rectangle, a right triangle, and a non-rectangular parallelogram.

Problem 1.3 Finding Areas

Students find areas of irregular figures drawn on a dot grid.

	Suggested Pacing	Materials for Students	Materials for Teachers	ACE Assignments
All	4 days	Centimeter rulers, calculators		
1.1	$1\frac{1}{2}$ days	Labsheet 1.1	Transparencies 1.1A and 1.1B (optional)	1–7, 26–28, 30, 35, 36
1.2	1 day	Labsheet 1.2, grid paper (optional; for special-needs students)	Transparency 1.2A and 1.2B (optional)	8–14, 29, 31, 37
1.3	1 day	Labsheet 1.3, geoboards (optional), Labsheet 1ACE Exercises 15–25	Transparency 1.3 (optional), overhead geoboard (optional)	15–25, 32–34, 38, 39
MR	$\frac{1}{2}$ day			

Driving Around Euclid

Goals

• Review the coordinate system

• Explore distances on a coordinate grid

In this problem, students review the concept of the coordinate grid and are introduced to the idea of finding distances between points. Students find two types of distances: distance along grid lines (represented by driving distances along city streets) and straight-line distance (represented by flying distance).

Launch 1.1

To launch this investigation, have students look at the map of Washington, D.C. in their books. Tell students that the system of streets is based on a coordinate grid. Discuss the features of the grid, which are listed in the student book.

Ask students to locate the intersection of 3rd Street and D Street and then share the location they found with the students sitting near them. Students should realize that there is more than one intersection fitting this description. In fact, there are four, one in each quadrant.

Suggested Question Ask:

• *What additional information could I give you so you know which intersection I am referring to?* (the quadrant the intersection is in)

Suggested Questions Discuss the Getting Ready questions. These questions can help you informally assess your students' understanding of coordinate grids.

• *Describe the location of each of these landmarks:*

George Washington University (Answers may vary slightly. Possible answer: 21st and H St. NW)

Dupont Circle (19th and P St. NW)

Benjamin Banneker Park (Answers may vary slightly. Possible answer: 10th and G St. SW)

The White House (Pennsylvania Ave. between 15th and 17th NW)

Union Station (1st and E St. NE)

• *How can you find the distance from Union Station to Dupont Circle?* (Measure the straight-line distance along Massachusetts Avenue. Note that, if we measure the distance in blocks, these blocks are not the same length as the north-south or the east-west blocks. Students may have a range of suggestions, and many students may struggle with this question.)

• *Find the intersection of G Street and 8th Street SE and the intersection of G Street and 8th Street NW. How are these locations related to the Capitol building?* (Possible answer: SE indicates that the location is southeast of the Capitol building. NW indicates that the location is northwest of the Capitol building. In addition, by counting the letters up to G and adding this to 8, we can determine that these places are each about 15 blocks from the Capitol.)

Next, talk about the map of the fictitious city of Euclid, which is also shown on Transparency 1.1B. Point out the origin (the location of City Hall), and discuss the meaning of the coordinates. Help students understand that a coordinate system is convenient for locating points, but only if we know where to count from and what scale is being used.

Suggested Questions Some questions might include:

• *What are the coordinates of City Hall?* $(0, 0)$

• *What are the coordinates of the art museum?* $(6, 1)$

• *What do the 6 and the 1 mean?* [They indicate that the art museum is 6 blocks to the right of (east of) and 1 block up from (north of) the origin, or City Hall.]

• *Is there more than one way to travel from City Hall to the art museum?* (Yes.)

• *What is the shortest distance, along the streets of Euclid, from City Hall to the art museum?* (7 blocks)

- *Is there more than one way to follow a shortest path from City Hall to the art museum?* (There are several, such as right 2 blocks, up 1 block, and right 4 blocks.)

- *A helicopter can fly directly from one location to another; it doesn't have to travel along the city streets. How can you determine the distance a helicopter travels to get from one point to another in Euclid?*

If no one suggests using a ruler, explain that because each centimeter on the map represents one block, you can use a centimeter ruler to find the straight-line distance, in blocks, between two points.

When students seem confident about reading map coordinates and finding distances, have them work individually or in pairs on the problem. Distribute Labsheet 1.1.

Explore 1.1

As students work, encourage them to look for connections between the coordinates of two points and the driving distance between them.

Suggested Questions Ask:

- *What do the first coordinates of the two points tell you about the distance between the points?* (The positive difference in the first coordinates is the horizontal distance between the points.)

- *What do the second coordinates tell you about the distance between the points?* (The positive difference in the second coordinates is the vertical distance between the points.)

- *How can you find the total driving distance?* (Add the horizontal and vertical distances.)

Check how students are measuring the distance a helicopter travels.

Summarize 1.1

Establish that students understand that the grid system makes it possible to refer to each landmark in Euclid by a unique pair of coordinates.

Suggested Questions Ask:

- *Why might it be important to be able to locate places in a city by using a simple system like grid coordinates?*

- *What information do you need to be able to locate a point on a grid?*

- *When we give the coordinates of a point in Euclid, where are we counting from? What scale are we using?* (We count from City Hall. The scale is in number of blocks.)

Be sure students can interpret the *x*- and *y*-coordinates of a point. Given a point on the grid, they should be able to name the coordinates. Given the coordinates of a point, they should be able to locate the point on the grid.

Suggested Questions Extend the coordinate idea to include non-integers:

- *Where in Euclid is the point* $(2, \frac{1}{4})$?

The driving distance between two points is the number of blocks a car would travel from one place to another. Talk with the class about finding the driving distance between two points given their coordinates. You might discuss these three examples:

- The hospital and the cemetery are on the same horizontal line. To find the distance between these points, find the positive difference in the *x*-coordinates.

- City Hall and the police station are on the same vertical line. To find the distance between these points, find the positive difference in the *y*-coordinates.

- The art museum and the gas station do not lie on the same horizontal or vertical line. To find the distance, find the positive difference in *x*-coordinates and the positive difference in *y*-coordinates, and add the two results.

If no one uses the term *absolute value* to describe the positive difference, you might bring it up yourself. The concept of using absolute value to express distance is explored in the grade 7 unit *Accentuate the Negative*, but you may want to review this idea with students.

Suggested Questions These questions might help clear up confusion:

- *To go from the art museum to the gas station, how many blocks do you travel in a horizontal direction?* (2 blocks)

- *How is this distance related to the coordinates of the points?* (It is the positive difference, or the absolute value of the difference, between the x-coordinates.)

- *To go from the art museum to the gas station, how many blocks do you travel in a vertical direction?* (3 blocks)

- *How is this distance related to the coordinates of the points?* (It is the positive difference, or the absolute value of the difference, between the y-coordinates.)

To help students think about direction, ask:

- *Suppose you are in Euclid and you are trying to find the library. Someone tells you it is 3 blocks from the stadium. Is this enough information for you to know how to get there?* (No.)

- *What information do you need to precisely locate the library?* (You need directions. For example, you might need to walk 3 blocks south of the stadium, or 2 blocks east and 1 block south from the stadium.)

Verify that everyone understands that to precisely locate a position on the grid, a vertical distance, a horizontal distance, and the direction of each must be given. A coordinate pair gives all of this information in a concise way.

In Question D, students should recognize that the flying distance is the length of the line segment connecting the points.

For Question E, review with the class why the helicopter distance is always shorter than or equal to the driving distance. This is an application of the *triangle inequality*, which students encountered in the grade 6 unit *Shapes and Designs*. The triangle inequality states that the sum of the lengths of any two sides of a triangle is greater than the length of the third side. The car distance is the sum of the lengths of two sides of a triangle; the helicopter distance is the length of the third side.

This is an opportunity to verify that students connect directions on a coordinate grid with map directions. Going left is traveling west; going up is traveling north, and so on.

1.1 Driving Around Euclid

PACING $1\frac{1}{2}$ days

Mathematical Goals

- Review the coordinate system
- Explore distances on a coordinate grid

Launch

Have students look at the map of Washington, D.C. in their books. Discuss the features of the street system, which are listed in the student book.

Discuss the Getting Ready questions.

Discuss the map of Euclid. Point out the origin (the location of City Hall), and discuss the meaning of the coordinates. Help students understand that a coordinate system is convenient for locating points.

- *What are the coordinates of City Hall?*
- *What are the coordinates of the art museum? What do the 6 and the 1 mean?*
- *What is the shortest distance, along the streets of Euclid, from City Hall to the art museum?*
- *Is there more than one shortest path from City Hall to the art museum?*
- *A helicopter can fly directly from one location to another; it doesn't have to travel along the city streets. How can you determine the distance a helicopter travels to get from one point to another in Euclid?*

Explain that because each centimeter on the map represents one block, a centimeter ruler could be used to find the straight-line distance, in blocks, between two points.

Have students work individually or in pairs on the problem.

Materials

- Centimeter rulers
- Transparencies 1.1A and 1.1B
- Labsheet 1.1

Explore

As students work, encourage them to look for connections between the coordinates of two points and the driving distance between them.

- *What do the first coordinates of the two points tell you about the distance between the points? What do the second coordinates tell you about the distance between the points?*
- *How can you find the total driving distance?*

Check how students are measuring the distance a helicopter travels.

Summarize

Talk with the class about finding the distance between two points given their coordinates.

- *To go from the art museum to the gas station, how many blocks do you travel in a horizontal direction? How is this distance related to the coordinates of the points?*

Materials

- Student notebooks

continued on next page

- *To go from the art museum to the gas station, how many blocks do you travel in a vertical direction? How is this distance related to the coordinates of the points?*

Help students think about direction. Verify that everyone understands that to precisely locate a position on the grid, a vertical distance, a horizontal distance, and the direction of each must be given. A coordinate pair gives all of this information in a concise way.

ACE Assignment Guide for Problem 1.1

Core 1–7
Other *Connections* 26–28, 30; *Extensions* 35, 36

Adapted For suggestions about adapting Exercises 1–6 and other ACE exercises, see the CMP *Special Needs Handbook*.

Answers to Problem 1.1

A. 1. $(4, 4)$

  2. $(6, -2)$

  3. $(-2, 3)$

B. 1. Pair 1: Go north (up) 4 blocks.

    Pair 2: Possible answer: Go east 6 blocks and then north 4 blocks.

    Pair 3: Possible answer: Go east 12 blocks and then north 5 blocks.

2. Pair 1: 4 blocks;
Pair 2: 10 blocks;
Pair 3: 17 blocks

C. Add the positive difference in the x-coordinates to the positive difference in the y-coordinates.

D. Pair 1: 4 blocks;
Pair 2: about 7.2 blocks;
Pair 3: 13 blocks

E. The helicopter distance will never be longer than the car distance. Generally, it will be shorter, unless the points are on the same vertical or horizontal line. In this case, the distances will be equal.

1.2 Planning Parks

Goals

- Review properties of quadrilaterals
- Connect properties of figures to coordinate representations
- Draw shapes in on a coordinate grid

In this problem, students review the properties of quadrilaterals and right triangles. Given the coordinates of two vertices of a polygon, they find the coordinates of other vertices so that the resulting shape will be a square, a non-square rectangle, a right triangle, or a non-rectangular parallelogram.

Launch 1.2

Introduce the context of planning parks in Euclid. Discuss the idea of describing the shapes of the parks by giving the vertices of their borders. Make sure students know what properties define a square, a right triangle, a rectangle, and a parallelogram.

Suggested Questions You may want to display a transparent grid of the Euclid map. Plot two points on the grid and ask questions like these:

- *Suppose we want to draw a right triangle with these points as two of the vertices. Locate such a right triangle and tell us the coordinates of the third vertex. How do you know that this is a right triangle?*

- *Now locate a rectangle that has one of its vertices at the origin. Tell us the coordinates of its vertices. How do you know that this is a rectangle?*

Ask similar questions about a square and a non-rectangular parallelogram. Take this opportunity to assess what students know about the properties of these polygons. Do they know that squares have sides of equal length and four right angles? Do they know that parallelograms have two pairs of parallel sides? Do they know that a figure's orientation does not matter? (For example, a square is still a square even if it is rotated to look like a "diamond.")

Now, describe Problem 1.2. Distribute Labsheet 1.2 (which contains two copies of the Euclid map), and have students work in groups of three or four on the problem.

Meeting Special Needs Some teachers have found that their special-needs students have been more successful using simple grid paper instead of Labsheet 1.2. You may find this provides less visual "noise" for some students.

Explore 1.2

Suggested Questions As students work, ask questions about the reasoning they are applying.

- *How did you figure out where to put the vertices so this park's sides would all be the same length?*

- *How did you determine where to put the vertices so opposite sides would be parallel?*

- *How did you decide where these vertices had to be to create right angles?*

Encourage students to discuss with the others in their group how they are finding the vertices of each shape so each student should be able to explain the group's strategies.

If students are struggling to find a square, suggest that they turn their papers slightly to make the given segment horizontal. It is sometimes easier for students to imagine an upright square on a tilted grid than a tilted square on an upright grid.

Summarize 1.2

Ask students to share their strategies for finding the vertices for each park shape. Here are some strategies students might have used:

- Use the concept of slope to check that opposite sides are parallel. Recall (from the grade 7 unit *Moving Straight Ahead*) that parallel lines have the same slope, and then use this fact to establish parallel sides.

- To find the slope of a line, students can count units up and units over to match the slope of an existing segment.

- Use the corner of a piece of paper to check for right angles.

- Use the fact that vertical and horizontal lines are perpendicular (they may recall that the slopes of perpendicular lines are negative reciprocals).

- Use a ruler or the marked edge of a piece of paper to check lengths.

- Use angle rulers to measure angles.

- Find the right triangle by dividing a rectangle or a square in half along one of its diagonals.

For Questions A, B, and D, if no one suggests a park in which the line segment connecting the given vertices is a diagonal rather than a side, introduce this possibility.

Check for Understanding

As a final summary, put a transparent grid on the overhead, and label x- and y-axes. Draw several parallelograms (including squares and non-square rectangles) on the grid.

Ask students to explain what is special about each figure. For example, a parallelogram is a trapezoid and it may be a square or a rectangle. A rhombus is a parallelogram and it could be a square or a rectangle. You may want to organize the relationships in a Venn diagram.

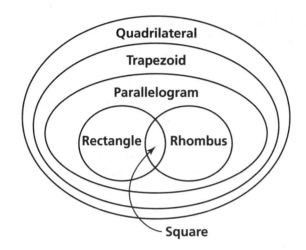

1.2 Planning Parks

Mathematical Goals

- Review properties of quadrilaterals
- Connect properties of figures to coordinate representations
- Draw shapes on a coordinate grid

Launch

Introduce the context of planning parks in Euclid. Discuss the idea of describing the shapes of the parks by giving the vertices of their borders. Make sure students know what properties define a square, a right triangle, a rectangle, and a parallelogram.

Display a coordinate grid on the overhead and discuss a few examples:

- *Suppose we want to draw a right triangle with these points as two of the vertices. Locate such a right triangle and tell us the coordinates of the third vertex. How do you know that this is a right triangle?*

Assess what students know about the properties of squares, rectangles, right triangles, and parallelograms.

Describe Problem 1.2. Distribute Labsheet 1.2 or centimeter grid paper, and have students work in groups of three or four on the problem.

Materials

- Centimeter rulers
- Transparencies 1.2A and 1.2B
- Labsheet 1.2
- Grid paper (optional)

Explore

Ask questions about the reasoning students are applying.

- *How did you figure out where to put the vertices so this park's sides would all be the same length?*
- *How did you determine where to put the vertices so opposite sides would be parallel?*
- *How did you decide where these vertices had to be to create right angles?*

Encourage students to discuss their reasoning with others in their group.

If students are struggling to find a square, suggest that they turn their papers slightly to make the given segment horizontal.

Summarize

Ask students to share their strategies for finding the vertices for each park shape. For Questions A, B, and D, if no one suggests a park in which the line segment connecting the given vertices is a diagonal rather than a side, introduce this possibility.

Materials

- Student notebooks

Check for Understanding

As a final summary, put a transparent grid on the overhead and label *x*- and *y*-axes. Draw several parallelograms (including squares and non-square rectangles) on the grid, and ask students what is special about each figure.

ACE Assignment Guide for Problem 1.2

Differentiated Instruction Solutions for All Learners

Core 8–10, 14
Other *Applications* 11–13; *Connections* 29, 31; *Extensions* 37; unassigned choices from earlier problems

Adapted For suggestions about adapting Exercises 8–10 and other ACE exercises, see the CMP *Special Needs Handbook.*
Connecting to Prior Units 29, 31: *Moving Straight Ahead, Thinking With Mathematical Models*

Answers to Problem 1.2

A. There are three possible pairs of vertices: (3, 5) and (0, 4); (5, −1) and (2, −2); and (3, 0) and (2, 3).

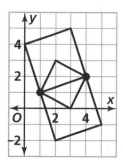

B. There are many possible pairs of vertices, including (6, −4) and (3, −5); (1, 2) and (4, 1); and (2, 0) and (3, 3).

C. There are several possible vertices, including (3, −5), (2, 3), and (5, −1).

D. There are many possible pairs of vertices, including (1, −1) and (4, 0); (2, 4) and (−1, 3); (0, 2) and (−3, 1); and (1, 3) and (4, 0).

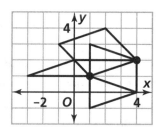

Goal

- Develop strategies for finding areas of irregular figures on a grid

In this problem, students begin by finding areas of figures on a dot grid. Then they move to the coordinate plane to find the area of one of the square parks from Problem 1.2. They will begin to see that, for some figures, it is easy to find areas by subdividing them and adding the areas of the component parts; other figures seem to need another approach.

Note: Many activities in this unit are classic geoboard problems. If you have access to geoboards, use them; students will enjoy exploring area with them. If your students have had experience with geoboards, this will go quickly. If not, spend time familiarizing students with them. Demonstrate how to form shapes and how to use extra rubber bands to subdivide a figure or to surround it with a rectangle. You might have students pair up and create figures for each other to find the area of irregular figures. An overhead geoboard would also be helpful in this problem.

Launch 1.3

Conduct the following short activity to introduce the idea of finding areas of figures drawn on a dot grid:

Draw a figure on a dot grid on the board, an overhead geoboard, or transparent dot paper. Choose a shape simple enough that students can easily find its area by subdividing it or by enclosing it in a rectangle. For example:

Ask students how they could find the area of the figure. Let students share their ideas. The two strategies students tend to use are outlined here. Students may have variations on these two strategies. It is not necessary to bring both of

these strategies out before students work on the problem, but you will want to address both in the summary.

Strategy 1:
Subdivide the figure. Find the area of each piece and add these areas to get the total area.

The area of this part is 2 square units.

The area of this part is 8 square units.

The total area is 10 square units.

Strategy 2:
Enclose the figure in a rectangle. Find the areas of the pieces surrounding the original shape. Then, subtract these areas from the area of the rectangle. This strategy is more efficient for certain figures such as the triangle in ACE Exercise 19.

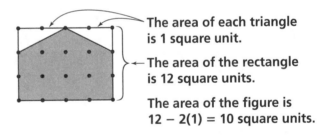

The area of each triangle is 1 square unit.

The area of the rectangle is 12 square units.

The area of the figure is 12 − 2(1) = 10 square units.

Have students explore the problem in pairs. Labsheet 1.3 contains the figures for Question A. Students may work on the labsheet, redraw the figures on dot paper, or construct them on geoboards.

Explore 1.3

In their work, students will review how to find areas of rectangles and triangles. Look for students who are actively applying this knowledge; they can share their strategies in the summary. Have some students put their work on large poster paper or a transparent grid. Students can count the number of units that cover the figure, or they can apply the rules for finding areas of rectangles and triangles. Some students may need help applying the rule for the area of a triangle, $A = \frac{1}{2}bh$. Help them to see that a triangle is half of a rectangle. This approach was used in the grade 6 unit *Covering and Surrounding*.

For additional practice and challenge, you may also want to have students work on ACE Exercises 15–20 at this time.

Summarize 1.3

As students share answers and strategies, help them generalize their methods for finding area.

Suggested Questions Ask:

- *We can find areas of some figures by subdividing them and adding the areas of the smaller figures. For which figures in this problem is using this method easy?* (Students will probably mention Figures 1, 2, 3, and 4, although students may also use this strategy on other figures.)

- *We can find areas of some figures by enclosing them in a rectangle and subtracting the areas of the unwanted parts from the rectangle's area. For which figures in this problem is using this method easy?* (Students' ideas will vary. Figure 5, for example, can be enclosed in a 2-by-3 rectangle. The areas of four triangles—two with area $\frac{1}{2}$ square unit and two with area 1 square unit—can then be subtracted from the rectangle's area, leaving 3 square units.)

- *Did you use different strategies for finding the area of the park on the coordinate grid?*

Some students may use the strategy of rearranging parts of a figure to form a rectangle or a triangle with an easy-to-find area. For example, see the answer given for Figure 3.

Students will need to be able to apply these methods for their future work in this unit, so make sure everyone can use at least one of them and explain why it works.

1.3 Finding Areas

Mathematical Goal

- Develop strategies for finding areas of irregular figures on a grid

Launch

Draw a simple figure on a dot grid. Ask students how they could find the area of the figure. Let students share their ideas. There are two main strategies students tend to use: subdividing the figure and finding the areas of the pieces; and enclosing the figure in a rectangle and subtracting the areas of the pieces outside the figure from the area of the rectangle. It is not necessary to discuss both strategies now, but you will want to address both in the summary.

Have students explore the problem in pairs. Students may work on Labsheet 1.3, redraw the figures on dot paper, or construct them on geoboards.

Materials
- Transparency 1.3
- Labsheet 1.3
- Geoboards (optional)
- Centimeter rulers

Explore

In their work, students will review how to find areas of rectangles and triangles. Look for students who are actively applying this knowledge; they can share their strategies in the summary. Some students may need help applying the rule for the area of a triangle $A = \frac{1}{2}bh$. Help them to see that a triangle is half of a rectangle.

You may want to have students work on ACE Exercises 15–20 at this time.

Summarize

As students share answers and strategies, help them generalize their methods for finding area.

- *We can find areas of some figures by subdividing them and adding the areas of the smaller figures. For which figures in this problem is using this method easy?*

- *We can find areas of some figures by enclosing them in a rectangle and subtracting the areas of the unwanted parts from the rectangle's area. For which figures in this problem is using this method easy?*

- *Did you use different strategies for finding the area of the park on the coordinate grid?*

Some students may use the strategy of rearranging parts of a figure to form a rectangle or a triangle with an easy-to-find area.

Students will need to be able to apply these methods for their future work in this unit, so make sure everyone can use at least one of them and explain why it works.

Materials
- Student notebooks

ACE Assignment Guide
for Problem 1.3

Core 15–25
Other *Connections* 32–34; *Extensions* 38, 39; unassigned choices from earlier problems

Adapted For suggestions about adapting ACE exercises, see the CMP *Special Needs Handbook*.
Connecting to Prior Units 32: *Bits and Pieces II*; 33, 38, 39: *Covering and Surrounding*; 34: *Accentuate the Negative*

Answers to Problem 1.3

A. **1.** 2 units^2

2. 1.5 units^2

3. 2 units^2

4. 4 units^2

5. 3 units^2

6. 4 units^2

7. 3.5 units^2

8. 6.5 units^2

9. 8.5 units^2

10. 8.5 units^2

B. 10 units^2 or 5 units^2, depending on which square the student chooses.

C. Possible strategies include subdividing figures and adding the areas of the smaller figures; enclosing figures in rectangles and then subtracting the areas of the unwanted parts; and rearranging parts to form a rectangle or triangle with an easy-to-find area.

Coordinate Grids

In this investigation, you will review how to use a coordinate grid to locate points in the plane. You will then explore how to find distances between points and areas of figures on a coordinate grid.

In the first two problems of this investigation, the coordinate grid is in the form of a street map of a fictional city called Euclid. The streets in most cities do not form perfect coordinate grids as they do in Euclid. However, many cities have streets that are at least loosely based on a coordinate system. One well-known example is Washington, D.C.

Did You Know?

The Lincoln Memorial stands at the west end of the National Mall in Washington, D.C. Built between 1914 and 1922, the memorial houses a 99-foot-tall statue of the first Republican president, Abraham Lincoln. The memorial celebrates Lincoln's accomplishments in uniting the divided nation and his quest to end slavery.

People often make speeches at the Lincoln Memorial, using the setting to strengthen their message. Martin Luther King, Jr. gave his famous "I have a Dream" speech at the memorial during the March on Washington in 1963.

Go Online
PHSchool.com
For: Information about the Lincoln Memorial
Web Code: ape-9031

Investigation 1 Coordinate Grids **5**

Notes _____

_____

_____

_____

The map on the next page shows the central part of Washington, D.C. The city's street system was designed by Pierre L'Enfant in 1791.

L'Enfant's design is based on a coordinate system. Here are some key features of L'Enfant's system:

- The north-south and east-west streets form grid lines.
- The origin is at the Capitol.
- The vertical axis is formed by North and South Capitol Streets.
- The horizontal axis is the line stretching from the Lincoln Memorial, through the Mall, and down East Capitol Street.
- The axes divide the city into four quadrants known as Northeast (NE), Southeast (SE), Southwest (SW), and Northwest (NW).

STUDENT PAGE

Notes

- Describe the locations of these landmarks:

  George Washington University

  Dupont Circle

  Benjamin Banneker Park

  The White House

  Union Station

- How can you find the distance from Union Station to Dupont Circle?

- Find the intersection of G Street and 8th Street SE and the intersection of G Street and 8th Street NW. How are these locations related to the Capitol Building?

STUDENT PAGE

Notes _____

_____

_____

_____

In mathematics, we use a coordinate system to describe the locations of points. Recall that horizontal and vertical number lines, called the *x*- and *y*-axes, divide the plane into four quadrants.

You describe the location of a point by giving its coordinates as an ordered pair of the form (*x*, *y*). On the coordinate grid at the right, four points are labeled with their coordinates.

1.1 Driving Around Euclid

The founders of the city of Euclid loved math. They named their city after a famous mathematician, and they designed the street system to look like a coordinate grid. The Euclideans describe the locations of buildings and other landmarks by giving coordinates. For example, the art museum is located at (6, 1).

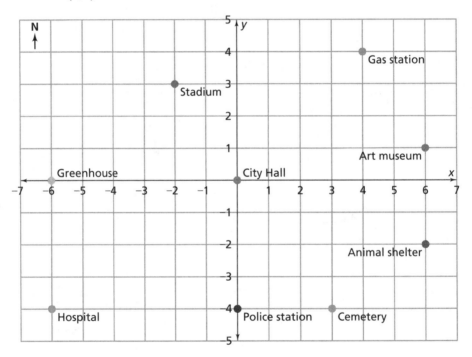

8   Looking for Pythagoras

Notes _____

_____

_____

_____

Problem **1.1** Locating Points and Finding Distances

A. Give the coordinates of each landmark.

   1. gas station

   2. animal shelter

   3. stadium

B. Euclid's chief of police is planning emergency routes. She needs to find the shortest driving route between the following pairs of locations:

Pair 1: the police station to City Hall

Pair 2: the hospital to City Hall

Pair 3: the hospital to the art museum

   1. Give precise directions for an emergency car route for each pair.

   2. For each pair, find the total distance in blocks a police car following your route would travel.

C. Suppose you know the coordinates of two landmarks in Euclid. How can you determine the shortest driving distance (in blocks) between them?

D. A helicopter can travel directly from one point to another. For each pair in Question B, find the total distance (in blocks) a helicopter would have to travel to get from the starting location to the ending location. You may find it helpful to use a centimeter ruler.

E. Will a direct helicopter route between two locations always be shorter than a car route? Explain your reasoning.

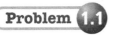 Homework starts on page 12.

Investigation 1 Coordinate Grids **9**

Notes _____

_____

_____

_____

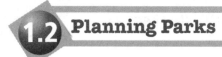

1.2 Planning Parks

The Euclid City Council is developing parks with geometric shapes. For some of the parks, the council gives the park designers constraints. For example, Descartes Park must have a border with vertices $(1, 1)$ and $(4, 2)$.

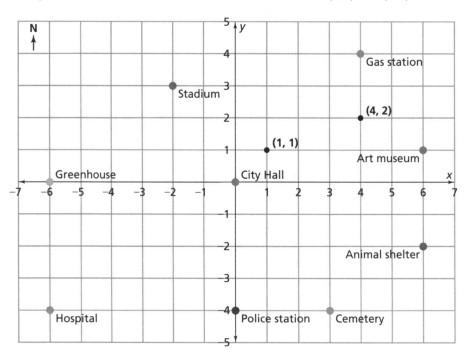

Problem 1.2 Shapes on a Coordinate Grid

Be prepared to explain your answers.

A. Suppose the park is to be a square. What could the coordinates of the other two vertices be? Give two answers.

B. Suppose the park is to be a nonsquare rectangle. What could the coordinates of the other two vertices be?

C. Suppose the park is to be a right triangle. What could the coordinates of the other vertex be?

D. Suppose the park is to be a parallelogram that is not a rectangle. What could the coordinates of the other two vertices be?

ACE Homework starts on page 12.

10 Looking for Pythagoras

Notes _____

_____

_____

_____

1.3 Finding Areas

Below are some park designs submitted to the Euclid City Council. To determine costs, the council needs to know the area of each park.

Problem 1.3 Finding Areas

Consider the horizontal or vertical distance between two adjacent dots to be 1 unit.

A. Find the area of each figure.

B. Find the area of one of the square parks you suggested in Problem 1.2.

C. Describe the strategies you used in Questions A and B.

ACE Homework starts on page 12.

active math
online

For: Dynamic Geoboard
Visit: PHSchool.com
Web Code: apd-2100

Investigation 1 Coordinate Grids **11**

Notes _____

_____

_____

_____

Applications

For Exercises 1–7, use the map of Euclid from Problem 1.1.

1. Give the coordinates of each landmark.

   a. art museum   **b.** hospital   **c.** greenhouse

2. What is the shortest driving distance from the animal shelter to the stadium?

3. What is the shortest driving distance from the hospital to the gas station?

4. What are the coordinates of a point halfway from City Hall to the hospital if you travel by taxi? Is there more than one possibility? Explain.

5. What are the coordinates of a point halfway from City Hall to the hospital if you travel by helicopter? Is there more than one possibility? Explain.

6. **a.** Which landmarks are 7 blocks from City Hall by car?

   b. Give precise driving directions from City Hall to each landmark you listed in part (a).

7. Euclid Middle School is located at the intersection of two streets. The school is the same driving distance from the gas station as the hospital is from the greenhouse.

   a. List the coordinates of each place on the map where the school might be located.

   b. Find the flying distance, in blocks, from the gas station to each location you listed in part (a).

Notes _____

_____

_____

_____

The points (0, 0) and (3, 2) are two vertices of a polygon with integer coordinates.

Homework Help Online
PHSchool.com
For: Help with Exercise 8
Web Code: ape-2108

8. What could the other two vertices be if the polygon is a square?

9. Suppose the polygon is a nonrectangular parallelogram. What could the other two vertices be?

10. What could the other vertex be if the polygon is a right triangle?

The points (3, 3) and (2, 6) are two vertices of a right triangle. Use this information for Exercises 11–13.

11. **Multiple Choice** Which point could be the third vertex of the right triangle?

   A. (3, 2)   **B.** (−1, 5)   **C.** (7, 4)   **D.** (0, 3)

12. Give the coordinates of at least two other points that could be the third vertex.

13. How many right triangles with vertices (3, 3) and (2, 6) can you draw? Explain.

14. Can the following points be connected to form a parallelogram? Explain.

   (1, 1)   (2, −2)   (4, 2)   (3, 5)

Find the area of each triangle. Copy the triangles onto dot paper if you need to.

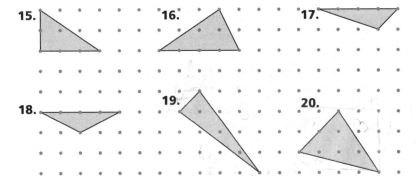

15.   16.   17.

18.   19.   20.

Notes _____

_____

_____

_____

(13) 30

Find the area of each figure, and describe the method you use. Copy the figures onto dot paper if you need to.

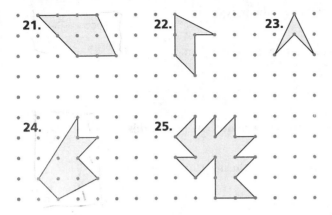

Connections

In the city of Euclid, the length of each block is 150 meters. Use this information and the map from Problem 1.1 for Exercises 26–28.

26. What is the shortest driving distance, in meters, from City Hall to the animal shelter?

27. What is the shortest driving distance, in meters, from the police station to the gas station?

28. Between which two landmarks is the shortest driving distance 750 meters?

29. When she solved Problem 1.2, Fabiola used slopes to help explain her answers.

   a. In Question A, she used slopes to show that adjacent sides of the figure were perpendicular. How might she have done this?

   b. In Question D, she used slopes to show that the figure was a parallelogram. How might she have done this?

Notes

30. Refer to the map of Euclid from Problem 1.1.

a. Matsu walks 2 blocks west from the police station and then walks 3 blocks north. Give the coordinates of the place where he stops.

b. Matsu's friend Cassandra is at City Hall. She wants to meet Matsu at his ending location from part (a). What is the shortest route she can take if she walks along city streets? Is there more than one possible shortest route?

c. Lei leaves the stadium and walks 3 blocks east, then 3 blocks south, then 2 blocks west, and finally 4 blocks north. Give the coordinates of the place where she stops.

d. Lei's sister Aida wants to meet her at her ending location from part (c). Aida is now at City Hall. What is the shortest route she can take if she walks along city streets? Is there more than one possible shortest route?

e. In general, how can you find the shortest route, walking along city streets, from City Hall to any point in Euclid?

Notes _____

_____

_____

_____

31. Below are equations for eight lines.

For: Multiple-Choice Skills Practice
Web Code: apa-2154

line 1: $y = 3x + 5$ line 2: $y = 0.5x + 3$

line 3: $y = 10 - 2x$ line 4: $y = 1 - \frac{1}{3}x$

line 5: $y = 7 + 3x$ line 6: $y = -2x + 1$

line 7: $y = 5 + 6x$ line 8: $y = 3x$

a. Which of the lines are parallel to each other?

b. Which of the lines are perpendicular to each other?

32. Marcia finds the area of a figure on dot paper by dividing it into smaller shapes. She finds the area of each smaller shape and writes the sum of the areas as $\frac{1}{2} \cdot 3 + \frac{1}{2} + \frac{1}{2} + 1$.

a. What is the total area of the figure?

b. On dot paper, draw a figure Marcia might have been looking at.

33. In the figure, a circle is inscribed in a square.

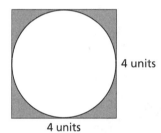

4 units

4 units

a. Find the area of the circle.

b. Find the area of the shaded region.

34. Refer to the ordered pairs to answer the questions. Do *not* plot the points on a grid. Explain each answer.

$(2, -3)$ $(3, -4)$ $(-4, -5)$ $(4, 5)$

$(-4, 6)$ $(-5, -5)$ $(0, -6)$ $(6, 0)$

a. Which point is farthest right?

b. Which point is farthest left?

c. Which point is above the others?

d. Which point is below the others?

STUDENT PAGE

Notes _____

_____

_____

_____

Extensions

35. Find a road map of your city or county. Figure out how to use the map's index to locate a city, street, or other landmark. How is finding a landmark by using an index description similar to and different from finding a landmark in Euclid by using its coordinates?

36. Use a map of your state to plan an airplane trip from your city or town to four other locations in your state. Write a set of directions for your trip that you could give to the pilot.

37. On grid paper, draw several parallelograms with diagonals that are perpendicular to each other. What do you observe about these parallelograms?

38. Find the areas of triangles *AST, BST, CST,* and *DST.* How do the areas compare? Why do you think this is true?

39. Find the areas of triangles *VMN, WMN, XMN, YMN,* and *ZMN.* How do the areas compare? Why do you think this is true?

Notes _____

_____

_____

_____

Mathematical Reflections 1

In this investigation, you solved problems involving coordinate grids. You located points, calculated distances and areas, and found vertices of polygons that satisfied given conditions. The following questions will help you summarize what you have learned.

Think about your answers to these questions. Discuss your ideas with other students and your teacher. Then write a summary of your findings in your notebook.

1. In the city of Euclid, how does the driving distance from one place to another compare to the flying distance?

2. Suppose you know the coordinates of two landmarks in Euclid. How can you find the distance between the landmarks?

3. Describe some strategies you can use to find areas of figures drawn on dot paper. Give examples if it helps you explain your thinking.

18   Looking for Pythagoras

Notes _____

_____

_____

_____

Answers

Investigation ⓵

ACE
Assignment Choices

Differentiated
Instruction
Solutions for All Learners

Problem 1.1
Core 1–7
Other *Connections* 26–28, 30; *Extensions* 35, 36

Problem 1.2
Core 8–10, 14
Other *Applications* 11–13; *Connections* 29, 31; *Extensions* 37; unassigned choices from earlier problems

Problem 1.3
Core 15–25
Other *Connections* 32–34; *Extensions* 38, 39; unassigned choices from earlier problems

Adapted For suggestions about adapting Exercises 1–6, 8–10, and other ACE exercises, see the CMP *Special Needs Handbook*.
Connecting to Prior Units 29, 31: *Moving Straight Ahead, Thinking With Mathematical Models*; 32: *Bits and Pieces II*; 33, 38, 39: *Covering and Surrounding*; 34: *Accentuate the Negative*

Applications

1. **a.** $(6, 1)$ **b.** $(-6, -4)$ **c.** $(-6, 0)$

2. 13 blocks   **3.** 18 blocks

4. There are many 10-block routes, but there are exactly five possible halfway points: $(-5, 0), (-4, -1), (-3, -2), (-2, -3),$ and $(-1, -4)$.

5. Because there is only one possible route, there is only one possible halfway point: $(-3, -2)$.

6. **a.** The art museum and the cemetery

   b. Possible answer: To get to the art museum, drive 6 blocks east, turn left, and go north 1 block. To get to the cemetery, drive 3 blocks east, turn right, and drive 4 blocks south.

7. **a.** The hospital is 4 blocks from the greenhouse. There are ten intersections on the map that are 4 blocks by car from the gas station: $(1, 5), (0, 4), (1, 3), (2, 2), (3, 1), (4, 0), (5, 1), (6, 2), (7, 3),$ and $(7, 5)$.

   b.

School Location	Flying Distance (blocks)
(1, 5)	≈ 3.2
(0, 4)	4
(1, 3)	≈ 3.2
(2, 2)	≈ 2.8
(3, 1)	≈ 3.2
(4, 0)	4
(5, 1)	≈ 3.2
(6, 2)	≈ 2.8
(7, 3)	≈ 3.2
(7, 5)	≈ 3.2

8. $(-2, 3)$ and $(1, 5)$; $(5, -1)$ and $(2, -3)$. There is a third possibility with non-integer coordinates, but students do not need to find this one.

9. There are infinitely many possible pairs, including $(2, 0)$ and $(5, 2)$; $(0, 2)$ and $(3, 4)$; $(0, -2)$ and $(3, 0)$; and $(2, -1)$ and $(5, 1)$.

10. There are infinitely many possible vertices, including $(0, 2), (3, 0), (4, -6)$ and $(5, -1)$. Any one of the vertices in Question 8 will work.

11. B

12. There are many possible vertices, including $(2, 3), (3, 6), (5, 7), (1, 4), (4, 5), (0, 2), (6, 4)$. (See the answer to Exercise 13.)

13. An infinite number of right triangles can be drawn. The third vertex can be located at any grid point on the line that goes through $(0, 2)$ and $(6, 4)$ (the line $y = \frac{1}{3}x + 2$) or on the line that goes through $(-1, 5)$ and $(5, 7)$ (the line $y = \frac{1}{3}x + \frac{16}{3}$). Each of these lines is perpendicular to the segment connecting $(3, 3)$ and $(2, 6)$, so these lines create the right angle for the triangle. Some students may express this idea as follows: Imagine a line starting from one of the given points and at a right angle to the given side. Any point along that line can be the third vertex of the triangle.

14. Yes. Opposite sides have equal lengths and slopes.

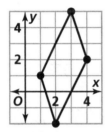

Note: The slopes may be compared intuitively at this time. Students may say the distance between parallel lines is always the same, or they may use left/right, up/down language to express this idea. Others may find the actual slopes.

15. 3 units^2 **16.** 4 units^2 **17.** 2 units^2

18. 2 units^2 **19.** 3.5 units^2 **20.** 5 units^2

21. 5 units^2 **22.** 2.5 units^2 **23.** 1 unit^2

24. 5.5 units^2 **25.** 8.5 units^2

Methods used in Exercises 21–25 will vary. Students may subdivide a figure into smaller squares and triangles and add their areas. They might surround a figure with a rectangle and subtract the areas of the shapes outside of the figure from the rectangle's area. For example, a square of area 4 units^2 can be drawn around the shape in Exercise 23, and the area of the three 1 unit^2 triangles can be subtracted, leaving an area of 1 unit^2.

Connections

26. 8 blocks · 150 m/block = 1,200 m

27. 12 blocks · 150 m/block = 1,800 m

28. 750 m ÷ 150 m/block = 5 blocks. City Hall and the Stadium are 5 blocks, or 750 meters, apart by car. So are the Cemetery and the Animal Shelter, and the Art Museum and the Gas Station.

29. a. She probably found the slopes of all four sides. The slopes of any two adjacent sides are negative reciprocals of each other, so they are perpendicular line segments (in other words, all four angles were 90°).

   b. She probably found the slopes of all four sides. Because the slopes of opposite sides were the same, they were parallel. because opposite sides of the quadrilateral were parallel, her figure was a parallelogram.

30. a. $(-2, -1)$

   b. There are three ways to find the shortest route. For example, Cassandra could walk 2 blocks west and 1 block south.

   c. $(-1, 4)$

   d. There are five ways to find the shortest route. For example, Aida could walk 1 block west and 4 blocks north.

   e. Figure out how many blocks east or west you have to go by comparing the x-coordinates of the two locations. Figure out how many blocks north or south you have to go by comparing the y-coordinates. The sum of these is the number of blocks in a shortest route.

31. a. Lines 1, 5, and 8; lines 3 and 6

   b. Lines 2 and 6; lines 3 and 2; lines 8 and 4; lines 1 and 4; lines 5 and 4

32. a. $3\frac{1}{2}$ units^2

   b. Answers will vary. Possible figure:

33. a. 4π, or about 12.56 units^2

   b. $16 - 4\pi$, or about 3.43 units^2

34. a. $(6, 0)$. It has the greatest x-coordinate.

  b. $(-5, -5)$. It has the least x-coordinate.

  c. $(-4, 6)$. It has the greatest y-coordinate.

  d. $(0, -6)$. It has the least y-coordinate.

Extensions

35. Road maps are typically partitioned into square areas by consecutive letters running along the sides of the map and consecutive numbers running along the top and bottom. This system is similar to a coordinate grid system, but the letters and numbers do not refer to points; they refer to regions. For example, anything in the top-left square might be in region A-1.

36. Answers will vary. Students should include compass directions as well as distances and will need to decide where the distances are to be measured from, such as airports or city centers. For example: Starting at the airport at Grand Rapids, go south 47 mi to the airport at Kalamazoo. From Kalamazoo, go northeast 60 mi to the airport at Lansing. From Lansing, go southeast 80 mi to the airport at Detroit.

For the Teacher You may want to point out that pilots need more exact directions than north, south, east, or west because the actual direction may be a few degrees east or west of due north.

37. Possible answer: For each parallelogram, all four sides are the same length. A rhombus is the only parallelogram with perpendicular diagonals. Students may only say that squares—rhombi with right angles—have perpendicular diagonals. You may want to encourage them to look for non-square rhombi.

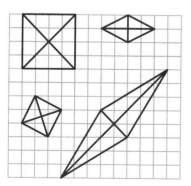

38. Each triangle has an area of 1 unit². They all have base length 1 unit and height 2 units.

39. Each triangle has an area of 3 units² because they all have base 3 units and height 2 units.

Possible Answers to Mathematical Reflections

1. Driving distances are the same as or greater than flying distances. If the two places do not lie on the same vertical or horizontal line, the flying distance is shorter because the car can't travel in a straight line between them, but the helicopter can.

2. Note that "distance" is intentionally vague. Students encountered two types of distances in Euclid: driving and flying. The flying distance corresponds to straight-line distance on the plane. Flying distances can be estimated with a ruler. Calculating flying distances exactly requires using the Pythagorean Theorem, which students do not yet know.

The driving distance between two landmarks is the sum of the positive differences of the x- and y-coordinates. In other words, the driving distance is the sum of the absolute value of the differences between the x- and y-coordinates.

3. Sometimes I just counted the units of area. Sometimes I subdivided the figure into smaller shapes like right triangles and rectangles, found the areas of the smaller shapes, and added them to get the large figure's area. Sometimes I enclosed the figure in a rectangle, found the area of the rectangle, and subtracted the areas of the figures that were not part of the enclosed figure.

Investigation 2 Squaring Off

Mathematical and Problem-Solving Goals

- Draw squares on 5 dot-by-5 dot grids and find their areas
- Introduce the concept of square root
- Understand square root geometrically, as the side length of a square with known area
- Use geometric understanding of square roots to find lengths of line segments on a dot grid

Summary of Problems

Problem 2.1 Looking for Squares

Students search for all the squares that can be drawn on a 5 dot-by-5 dot grid. In the process, they begin to see how the area of a square relates to its side length.

Problem 2.2 Square Roots

Students are introduced to the concept of square root. They learn that the positive square root of a number is the side length of a square with that number as area.

Problem 2.3 Using Squares to Find Lengths

Students find the lengths of segments on a dot grid by drawing squares with the segment as the side length. The length of the segment is the square root of the square's area.

	Suggested Pacing	Materials for Students	Materials for Teachers	ACE Assignments
All	4 days	Centimeter rulers, calculators, student notebooks		
2.1	1 day	Labsheet 2.1	Transparency 2.1 (optional)	1–3, 42, 47, 48
2.2	$1\frac{1}{2}$ days		Transparency 2.2 (optional)	4–34
2.3	1 day	Labsheet 2.3, geoboards (optional)	Transparencies 2.3A–C (optional)	35–41, 43–46, 49–53
MR	$\frac{1}{2}$ day			

Looking for Squares

Goal

- Draw squares on 5 dot-by-5 dot grids and find their areas

In this problem, students draw squares of various sizes on 5 dot-by-5 dot grids. In the process, they begin to see how the area of a square relates to the length of its sides.

Launch 2.1

Display Transparency 2.1 or draw a 5 dot-by-5 dot grid on the board. Draw a unit square on the grid and label it with the numeral 1.

Suggested Question Ask:

- *I have drawn a square with an area of 1 square unit on this 5 dot-by-5 dot grid. Can someone come up and draw a square with a different area?*

Explain that students are to search for all the different sizes (areas) of squares that will fit on a 5 dot-by-5 dot grid. Distribute Labsheet 2.1 and have students work on the problem in groups of two or three.

Explore 2.1

Some students may find "upright" squares easily (such as a square with an area of 9 square units) but have difficulty finding "tilted" squares (such as a square with an area of 10 square units).

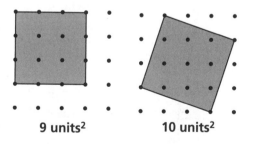

9 units²   **10 units²**

If students have difficulty identifying tilted squares, display one on the board or overhead. Start with a square of area 2.

If some students find the same size square more than once, remind them to check the area of each square they draw to verify that the areas are different.

You might want to have some groups put their work on large poster paper to refer to in the discussion and in the rest of the unit.

Summarize 2.1

Ask students to share the various squares they found. Ask them to draw them on Transparency 2.1. Continue until all eight squares are displayed. (If students do not offer all eight, suggest the missing ones yourself.) Discuss the strategies students used to find the squares.

Suggested Questions Ask:

- *Which squares were easy to find? Why?* (Upright squares, because their sides align with the horizontal and vertical lines of dots in the grid)

- *Which squares were not easy to find? Why?* (Tilted squares, because their sides must meet at right angles, but they do not align with horizontal and vertical lines of dots in the grid)

- *How do you know that the figures you drew were squares?* (I checked that the side lengths were equal and all angles were right angles or determined that the sides were perpendicular.)

2.1 Looking for Squares

Mathematical Goal

- Draw squares on 5 dot-by-5 dot grids and find their areas

Launch

Display Transparency 2.1 or draw a 5 dot-by-5 dot grid on the board. Draw a unit square on the grid and label it with the numeral 1.

- *I have drawn a square with an area of 1 square unit on this 5 dot-by-5 dot grid. Can someone come up and draw a square with a different area?*

Explain that students are to search for all the different sizes (areas) of squares that will fit on a 5 dot-by-5 dot grid. Distribute Labsheet 2.1 and have students work on the problem in groups of two or three.

Materials
- Transparency 2.1
- Labsheet 2.1
- Centimeter rulers or other straightedges

Explore

If students have difficulty identifying tilted squares, display one on the board or overhead. Start with a square of area 2.

Remind students to check the area of each square they draw to verify that the areas are all different.

Summarize

Ask students to share the various squares they found as you draw them on Transparency 2.1. Continue until all eight squares are displayed. (If students do not offer all eight, suggest the missing ones yourself.) Discuss the strategies students used to find the squares.

- *Which squares were easy to find? Why?*
- *Which squares were not easy to find? Why?*
- *How did you determine that your figure was a square?*

Materials
- Student notebooks

ACE Assignment Guide for Problem 2.1

Core 1, 2, 42
Other *Applications* 3; *Extensions* 47, 48

Adapted For suggestions about adapting ACE exercises, see the CMP *Special Needs Handbook.*
Connecting to Prior Units 42: *Shapes and Designs, Covering and Surrounding, Moving Straight Ahead*

Answers to Problem 2.1

A. Eight different areas are possible:

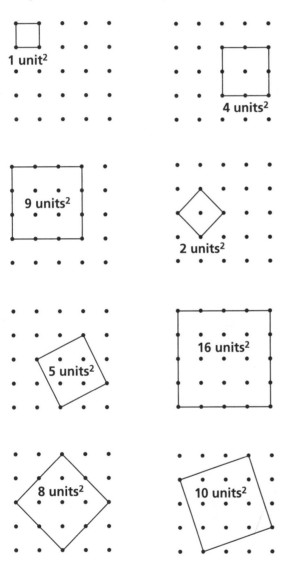

B. For the examples in this problem, all the upright squares have whole-number side lengths. Some tilted squares also have whole-number side lengths. An example of this (a tilted square with area 25 units^2) will be seen in Problem 2.3.

2.2 Square Roots

Goals

- Introduce the concept of square root

- Understand square root geometrically, as the side length of a square with known area

In this problem, the concept of square root is introduced in the context of the relationship between the area of a square and the length of its sides.

Launch 2.2

Discuss the side length of the square with an area of 4 square units. Draw the square on the board or overhead.

Suggested Questions

- *This square has an area of 4 square units. What is the length of a side?* (2 units)

- *How do you know your answer is correct?* (You can easily count 2 units along any side, and $2 \cdot 2 = 4$, or $2^2 = 4$.)

Introduce the concept of *square root*.

- *What number multiplied by itself is 4?* (2) *We can say this another way: The* square root *of 4 is 2.*

- *A square root of a number is a number that when squared, or multiplied by itself, equals the number. 2 is a square root of 4 because $2 \cdot 2 = 4$.*

- *Is there another number you can multiply by itself to get 4?* (Yes, −2)

Write $\sqrt{4}$ on the board.

- *This notation means the positive square root of 4.*

Add to the text on the board to get $\sqrt{4} = 2$.

- *If we want to denote the negative square root, we need to add a negative symbol.*

Write $-\sqrt{4} = -2$ on the board.

- *Because we are working with lengths, we will be using only the positive square roots of numbers.*

On the board or overhead, draw a square with an area of 2 square units on a dot grid.

2 units²

Suggested Questions Discuss the Getting Ready questions.

- *What is the side length of a square with an area of 2 square units?* ($\sqrt{2}$ units)

- *Is this length greater than 1 unit? Is it greater than 2 units?* (It is between 1 and 2 units. Students may not be able to answer the first question yet because $1^2 = 1$ and $2^2 = 4$.)

- *Is 1.5 a good estimate for $\sqrt{2}$? Explain.* (It depends on how much accuracy we want. $1.5 \cdot 1.5 = 2.25$, which is not that close to 2, so one could say it is not a good estimate.)

- *Can you find a better estimate for $\sqrt{2}$?* (1.4 is a better estimate because $1.4 \cdot 1.4 = 1.96$, which is closer to 2.)

When students have some understanding of the concept of a square root, have them work on the problem in groups of two or three. Remind them that they should use a calculator only when the text asks them to do so. There is some important estimation work that would be trivialized by premature use of a calculator.

Explore 2.2

Ask students how they know their answers for Questions A and B are correct. Ask them how they could check their answers.

As the groups finish Questions A and B, ask them to find the negative square roots of 1, 9, 16, and 25 as well. Check their work to see if they are using the square root symbol correctly.

Talk about the side length of the square with an area of 2 square units.

- *How can you prove that the area of this square is 2 square units?* (Subdivide the square into smaller regions and add their areas, or enclose the square in a larger square and subtract the areas of the four triangles outside the original square from the area of the larger square.)

- *What is the exact length of a side of this square?* ($\sqrt{2}$ units)

- *You estimated $\sqrt{2}$ by measuring a side of the square. What did you get?* (Most students will get about 1.4.)

- *Is this the exact value of $\sqrt{2}$? Does 1.4 squared equal 2?* (No, $1.4^2 = 1.96$, so 1.4 is too small.)

- *You also found $\sqrt{2}$ by using the square root key on your calculator. What value did your calculator give?* (1.414213562)

Write this number on the board.

- *Enter this number into your calculator and square it. Is the result exactly equal to 2?* (No; you get 1.999999999.)

- *So the value you get by measuring and the value you get with your calculator are both estimates.*

For the Teacher If you use a calculator to find $\sqrt{2}$, and then square the calculator's result, you *will* get 2. However, if you enter the estimate and square it, you will get 1.999999999.

Emphasize that the value students got by measuring and the value they got using a calculator are only approximate values of $\sqrt{2}$. The exact value is $\sqrt{2}$. Note that $\sqrt{2} \cdot \sqrt{2} = \sqrt{4} = 2$.

Continue the discussion with $\sqrt{5}$:

- *What number multiplied by itself is 5?* ($\sqrt{5}$)

- *Which two whole numbers is $\sqrt{5}$ between?* (2 and 3)

- *How do you know this?* (2^2 is 4 and 3^2 is 9. So, 5 is between 2^2 and 3^2. This means $\sqrt{5}$ is between 2 and 3.)

- *Is $\sqrt{5}$ closer to 2 or 3?* (2. Possible explanation: 2.5^2 is 6.25. Because 5 is less than 6.25, $\sqrt{5}$ must be less than 2.5, so it is closer to 2.)

Ask some students to suggest decimal approximations for $\sqrt{5}$. As a class, use a calculator to multiply each approximation by itself to check whether the result is 5.

Discuss the answer to Question E.

- *What are the side lengths of all the squares you found in Problem 2.1?* ($1, \sqrt{2}, 2, \sqrt{5}, \sqrt{8}, 3, \sqrt{10}$, and 4)

- *Which is the least side length? Which is the greatest?*

You might display a number line on the board or overhead and invite students to mark and label the location of each side length. To know where to place some of the values, they may need to use a calculator to find approximate square roots or use reasoning similar to that used in Question D to find an estimate for $\sqrt{5}$.

Question E leads into Problem 2.3, in which students find all the different lengths of line segments that can be drawn on a 5 dot-by-5 dot grid.

Mathematical Goals

- Introduce the concept of square root
- Understand square root geometrically, as the side length of a square with known area

Launch

Discuss the side length of the square with an area of 4 square units.

- *What is the length of each side? How do you know your answer is correct?*

Introduce the concept of square root.

- *What number multiplied by itself is 4?* We say the square root *of 4 is 2.*
- *A square root of a number is a number that when squared, or multiplied by itself, equals the number. 2 is a square root of 4 because 2 · 2 = 4.*
- *Is there another number you can multiply by itself to get 4?*

Introduce square root notation. Write $\sqrt{4} = 2$ and $-\sqrt{4} = -2$ on the board.

Draw a square with an area of 2 square units on a dot grid. Ask:

- *What is the side length of this square? Is it greater than 1? Is it greater than 2? Is 1.5 a good estimate for $\sqrt{2}$? Can you find a better estimate?*

When students understand the concept of square root, have them work on the problem in groups of two or three. Remind students that they should use a calculator only when the text asks them to do so.

Materials

- Transparency 2.2

Vocabulary

- square root

Explore

Ask students how they know their answers for Questions A and B are correct. Ask them how they could check their answers.

Ask students to find the negative square roots of 1, 9, 16, and 25 as well. Check their work to see if they are using the square root symbol correctly.

Summarize

Talk about the side length of the square with an area of 2 square units.

- *How can you prove that the area of this square is 2 square units?*
- *What is the exact length of a side of this square?*
- *You estimated $\sqrt{2}$ by measuring a side of the square. What did you get? Is this the exact value of $\sqrt{2}$?*
- *You also found $\sqrt{2}$ by using the square root key on your calculator. What value did your calculator give? Enter this number into your calculator and square it. Is the result exactly equal to 2?*

Materials

- Student notebooks

continued on next page

Emphasize that the results found by measuring and with a calculator are only approximate values for $\sqrt{2}$.

Ask students for decimal approximations for $\sqrt{5}$. As a class, use a calculator to square each approximation to check whether the result is 5.

Discuss Question E.

- *What are the side lengths of all the squares you found in Problem 2.1? Which is the least side length? Which is the greatest?*

You could have the students write the lengths on a number line.

ACE Assignment Guide for Problem 2.2

Core 4–6, 10, 14–18
Other *Applications* 7–9, 11–13, 19–34; unassigned choices from earlier problems

Adapted For suggestions about ACE exercises, see the CMP *Special Needs Handbook*.

Answers to Problem 2.2

A. 1. 1 unit; 3 units; 4 units; 5 units
  2. $\sqrt{1} = 1, \sqrt{9} = 3, \sqrt{16} = 4, \sqrt{25} = 5.$
B. 1. 144 units^2; 6.25 units^2
  2. $\sqrt{144} = 12, \sqrt{6.25} = 2.5.$
C. 1. About 1.4
  2. Using 1.4 as the side length gives an area of $1.4 \cdot 1.4 = 1.96$ units^2, which is not equal to 2 units^2.
  3. Possible answer: 1.41421356237. The exact number of digits depends on the type of calculator.
  4. The ruler estimate gives only the first few digits of the calculator estimate. In our case, the ruler estimate has only one decimal place. The calculator gives greater accuracy, but its answer is also an approximation, just as the ruler answer is.

D. 1. 2 and 3. Because 5 falls between 2^2 and 3^2, $\sqrt{5}$ must be between 2 and 3.
  2. 2 is closer to $\sqrt{5}$. Possible explanation: 2.5^2 is 6.25. Because 5 is less than 6.25, $\sqrt{5}$ must be less than 2.5.

  For the Teacher We cannot know which whole number a square root is closer to by comparing the squares of the numbers. Consider the preceding example: 6.25 is closer to 4 than to 9, yet $\sqrt{6.25} = 2.5$ is exactly halfway between 2 and 3. This fact is not the point of this problem and need not be made with students just beginning to understand square roots.

  3. 2.24. This estimate can be found by trial and error as follows: Find the squares of 2.1, 2.2, 2.3, and so on. You'll find that 5 is between 2.3^2 and 2.4^2. So, $\sqrt{5}$ must be between 2.2 and 2.3. Then, find the squares of 2.21, 2.22, 2.23, and so on. You'll find that $\sqrt{5}$ is between 2.23 and 2.24. Next, find the squares of 2.231, 2.232, 2.233, and so on. You'll find that 5 is between 2.236^2 and 2.237^2. This means that $\sqrt{5}$ rounded to the hundredths place is 2.24.

E. 1 unit, $\sqrt{2}$ units, 2 units, $\sqrt{5}$ units, $\sqrt{8}$ units, 3 units, $\sqrt{10}$ units, and 4 units

Goal

- Use geometric understanding of square roots to find lengths of line segments on a dot grid

In this problem, students develop a strategy for finding the distance between dots on a grid by examining the line segment between the dots. To find the length of the line segment, students draw a square with the segment as one side, find the area of the square, and then find the square root of the area.

Launch 2.3

As a class, list all the side lengths (in units) students have found so far in their work with 5 dot-by-5 dot grids: 1, $\sqrt{2}$, 2, $\sqrt{5}$, $\sqrt{8}$, 3, $\sqrt{10}$, and 4.

Suggested Question Ask:

- *Can you draw a line segment on a 5 dot-by-5 dot grid with a length that is different from these?*

On Transparency 2.3A, draw the segment the class suggests, or draw one of your own. Here is an example:

Suggested Questions Ask:

- *How do you know the length of this segment is different from others you have found?*

Students might mention ways to informally measure the length of the segment, or they might suggest comparing the segment to others that are a bit shorter or longer.

- *How might we find the actual length of this line segment?*

Some students might suggest drawing a square using this segment as a side and then calculating the segment's length from the square's area. If no one suggests this method, remind students of the connection they found between the area of a square and the length of a side. Walk through this process for the segment you drew.

Explain to students that the squares they draw will extend beyond the 5 dot-by-5 dot grid. For example, here is the square for the segment to the left below. The area of the square is 13 square units, so the length of the segment is $\sqrt{13}$ units.

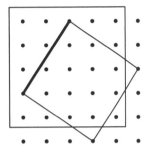

When students understand the process, distribute Labsheet 2.3 and have students explore the problem in groups of three or four. If geoboards are available, students can put two or more of them together to work on this problem.

Explore 2.3

Groups do not need to find all 14 possible lengths. However, be sure every student is able to draw a square on a line segment and find the length of the segment. You may want to have some groups put their work on poster paper for discussion.

Going Further

Ask students who finish to count the different lengths that can be drawn on a 2 dot-by-2 dot grid, a 3 dot-by-3 dot grid, and a 4 dot-by-4 dot grid. Have them look for a pattern that will help them to predict the number of possible lengths on a 6 dot-by-6 dot and 7 dot-by-7 dot grid. For an n dot-by-n dot grid, there are all of the lengths that were in an $(n - 1)$ dot-by-$(n - 1)$ dot grid, plus n more. Therefore, a 6 dot-by-6 dot grid has the 14 lengths from the 5 dot-by-5 dot grid, plus 6 more, for a total of 20. The 7 dot-by-7 dot grid has 20 + 7, or 27 lengths.

Ask students to share the lengths they found. Draw the lengths on Transparency 2.3A or show them on an overhead geoboard. Continue until all 14 lengths are displayed. Ask students to share strategies they used to make sure they had all the lengths. Arrange the lengths in an orderly way (see below).

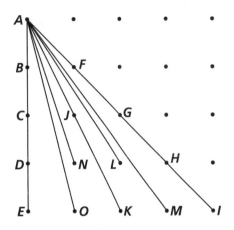

Segment	Length (units)
AB	1
AC	2
AD	3
AE	4
AF	$\sqrt{2}$
AG	$\sqrt{8}$, or $2\sqrt{2}$
AH	$\sqrt{18}$, or $3\sqrt{2}$
AI	$\sqrt{32}$, or $4\sqrt{2}$
AJ	$\sqrt{5}$
AK	$\sqrt{20}$, or $2\sqrt{5}$
AL	$\sqrt{13}$
AM	5
AN	$\sqrt{10}$
AO	$\sqrt{17}$

Discuss the strategies students used to find the lengths. In some cases, students may have used relationships between line segments rather than drawing a square. For example, the length of

segment AG is twice that of segment AF, so it is $2\sqrt{2}$. The area of a square with a side length of $2\sqrt{2}$ is 4 times the area of the similar square with an area of 2, or $4 \cdot 2 = 8$. Thus $\sqrt{8} = 2\sqrt{2}$. Students who find the length of AG by drawing a square will get $\sqrt{8}$. If your class is ready, talk about this equivalence: $\sqrt{8} = \sqrt{4 \cdot 2} = \sqrt{4} \cdot \sqrt{2} = 2\sqrt{2}$. Or, have students use a calculator to evaluate the various expressions.

Suggested Questions To test their understanding of A(3), ask the following:

- *Between what two whole numbers does $\sqrt{17}$ lie?* (4 and 5)

- *Which whole number is it closer to?* (It is closer to 4 because $4.5^2 = 20.25$, so $\sqrt{17}$ is less than 4.5. A calculator tells us that it is about 4.123105626.)

- *Between what two whole numbers does $\sqrt{32}$ lie?* (5 and 6)

- *How many of the lengths we have listed would you have found on a 4-dot-by-4-dot grid?* (1, 2, and 3 as side lengths of upright squares; $\sqrt{2}, \sqrt{5}, \sqrt{8}, \sqrt{10}, \sqrt{13}$, and $\sqrt{18}$ as side lengths of tilted squares)

- *What is $\sqrt{2} \times \sqrt{2}$?* (2) *Why?* (Because $\sqrt{2}$ is the side length of a square with area 2)

- *What is $\sqrt{5} \times \sqrt{5}$?* (5) *Why?*

If Question C has not been discussed, be sure students share their strategies. Ask if there are other line segments whose lengths can be expressed in more than one way. For example, $3\sqrt{2} = \sqrt{18}$ and $2\sqrt{5} = \sqrt{20}$.

- *Are there lengths that cannot be expressed in more than one way?* (Yes, $\sqrt{2}, \sqrt{5} \dots$)

Check for Understanding

Draw another segment on a dot grid. Ask the class to express its exact length using a $\sqrt{}$ symbol and then to tell which two whole numbers the length is between.

- *Which whole number is it closer to? How do you know?*

- *Is there another way to express this length?* (*For example, $\sqrt{8} = 2\sqrt{2}$*)

2.3 Using Squares to Find Lengths

PACING 1 day

Mathematical Goal

- Use geometric understanding of square roots to find lengths of line segments on a dot grid

Launch

List all the side lengths that students have found so far in their work with 5 dot-by-5 dot grids: $1, \sqrt{2}, 2, \sqrt{5}, \sqrt{8}, 3, \sqrt{10}$, and 4.

- *Can you draw a line segment on a 5 dot-by-5 dot grid with a length that is different from these?*

On Transparency 2.3A, draw the segment the class suggests, or draw one of your own.

- *How do you know the length of this segment is different from others you have found? How might we find the actual length of this line segment?*

Explain to students that the squares they draw in the problem will extend beyond the 5 dot-by-5 dot grid. Have students explore the problem in groups of three or four.

Materials
- Transparency 2.3A
- Labsheet 2.3
- Centimeter rulers
- Geoboards (optional)

Explore

Groups do not need to find all 14 possible lengths. However, be sure every student is able to draw a square on a line segment and find the length of the segment.

Materials
- Transparencies 2.3B and 2.3C

Summarize

Ask students to share the lengths they found. Draw the lengths on Transparency 2.3 or show them on an overhead geoboard. Continue until all 14 line segment lengths are displayed. Ask the class for strategies they used to make sure they had all the lengths.

Discuss the strategies that students used to find the lengths. If your class is ready, talk about equivalence: $\sqrt{8} = \sqrt{4 \cdot 2} = \sqrt{4} \cdot \sqrt{2} = 2\sqrt{2}$.

Part (3) of Question A asks students for approximations of some of the square roots they have found. To test their understanding, ask the following:

- *Between what two whole numbers does $\sqrt{17}$ lie? Which whole number is it closer to?*

- *Between what two whole numbers does $\sqrt{32}$ lie?*

- *How many of the lengths we have listed would you have found on a 4 dot-by-4 dot grid? What is $\sqrt{2} \cdot \sqrt{2}$? What is $\sqrt{5} \cdot \sqrt{5}$? Why?*

If Question C has not been discussed, be sure students share their strategies. Share Transparencies 2.3B and 2.3C with your students.

Materials
- Student notebooks

continued on next page

Summarize
continued

Check for Understanding

Draw another segment on a dot grid. Ask the class to express its exact length using a $\sqrt{}$ symbol and then to tell which two whole numbers the length is between.

ACE Assignment Guide for Problem 2.3

Core 35–37, 41
Other *Applications* 38–40; *Connections* 43–46; *Extensions* 49–53; unassigned choices from earlier problems

Adapted For suggestions about adapting Exercise 41 and other ACE exercises, see the CMP *Special Needs Handbook.*
Connecting to Prior Units 43: *Covering and Surrounding;* 45: *Bits and Pieces III;* 46: *Stretching and Shrinking*

Answers to Problem 2.3

A. 1 and 2.

The possible lengths in increasing order are $1, \sqrt{2}, 2, \sqrt{5}, \sqrt{8}, 3, \sqrt{10}, \sqrt{13}, 4, \sqrt{17}, \sqrt{18}, \sqrt{20}, 5,$ and $\sqrt{32}$. See the Summarize section for pictures and more information.

3.

Exact Length	Decimal Approximation
$\sqrt{2}$	1.4
$\sqrt{5}$	2.2
$\sqrt{8}$	2.8
$\sqrt{10}$	3.2
$\sqrt{13}$	3.6
$\sqrt{17}$	4.1
$\sqrt{18}$	4.2
$\sqrt{20}$	4.5
$\sqrt{32}$	5.7

B. Both are correct. The length of *AC* is twice the length of *AB*. Because the length of *AB* is $\sqrt{2}$ (being a side of the small square), the length of *AC* is 2 times $\sqrt{2}$, or $2\sqrt{2}$. We can also find the length of *AC* directly by making it a side of a square (the large square in the picture below) whose area is 8. So, the length of *AC* also equals $\sqrt{8}$. So, $2\sqrt{2} = \sqrt{8}$.

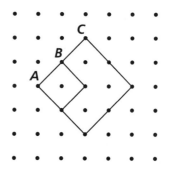

C. 1. $\sqrt{40}$, or $2\sqrt{10}$

2. Some examples are $\sqrt{17}, \sqrt{13}, \sqrt{5}$.

Investigation 2

Squaring Off

In this investigation, you will explore the relationship between the side lengths and areas of squares and use that relationship to find the lengths of segments on dot grids.

2.1 Looking for Squares

You can draw squares with different areas by connecting the points on a 5 dot-by-5 dot grid. Two simple examples follow.

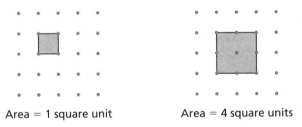

Area = 1 square unit   Area = 4 square units

In this problem, you will explore other possible areas.

Problem 2.1 Looking for Squares

A. On 5 dot-by-5 dot grids, draw squares of various sizes by connecting dots. Draw squares with as many different areas as possible Label each square with its area. Include at least one square whose sides are not horizontal and vertical.

B. Analyze your set of squares and describe the side lengths you found.

ACE Homework starts on page 23.

Notes _____

_____

_____

_____

Square Roots

The area of a square is the length of a side multiplied by itself. This can be expressed by the formula $A = s \cdot s$, or $A = s^2$.

If you know the area of a square, you can work backward to find the length of a side. For example, suppose a square has an area of 4 square units. To find the length of a side, you need to figure out what positive number multiplied by itself equals 4. Because $2 \cdot 2 = 4$, the side length is 2 units. We call 2 a **square root** of 4.

This square has an area of 4 square units. The length of each side is the square root of 4, or 2, units.

In general, if $A = s^2$, then s is a square root of A. Because $2 \cdot 2 = 4$ and $-2 \cdot -2 = 4$, 2 and -2 are both square roots of 4. Every positive number has two square roots. The number 0 has only one square root, 0.

If N is a positive number, then $\sqrt{N}$ indicates the positive square root of N. For example, $\sqrt{4} = 2$. The negative square root of 4 is $-\sqrt{4} = -2$.

If the area of a square is known, then square roots can be used to describe the length of a side of the square.

Getting Ready for Problem 2.2

The area of a square is the side length squared.

- What is the side length of a square with an area of 2 square units?

- Is this length greater than 1? Is it greater than 2?

- Is 1.5 a good estimate for $\sqrt{2}$?

- Can you find a better estimate for $\sqrt{2}$?

Notes

In this problem, use your calculator only when the question directs you to.

A. 1. Find the side lengths of squares with areas of 1, 9, 16, and 25 square units.

   2. Find the values of $\sqrt{1}$, $\sqrt{9}$, $\sqrt{16}$, and $\sqrt{25}$.

B. 1. What is the area of a square with a side length of 12 units? What is the area of a square with a side length of 2.5 units?

   2. Find the missing numbers.

$$\sqrt{\blacksquare} = 12 \qquad \sqrt{\blacksquare} = 2.5$$

C. Refer to the square with an area of 2 square units you drew in Problem 2.1. The exact side length of this square is $\sqrt{2}$ units.

   1. Estimate $\sqrt{2}$ by measuring a side of the square with a centimeter ruler.

   2. Calculate the area of the square, using your measurement from part (1). Is the result exactly equal to 2?

   3. Use the square root key on your calculator to estimate $\sqrt{2}$.

   4. How does your ruler estimate compare to your calculator estimate?

D. 1. Which two whole numbers is $\sqrt{5}$ between? Explain.

   2. Which whole number is closer to $\sqrt{5}$? Explain.

   3. Without using the square root key on your calculator, estimate the value of $\sqrt{5}$ to two decimal places.

E. Give the exact side length of each square you drew in Problem 2.1.

ACE Homework starts on page 23.

Notes _____

_____

_____

_____

Using Squares to Find Lengths

You can use a square to find the length of a segment connecting dots on a grid. For example, to find the length of the segment on the left, draw a square with the segment as a side. The square has an area of 5 square units, so the segment has length $\sqrt{5}$ units.

Problem 2.3 Using Squares to Find Lengths

A. 1. On 5 dot-by-5 dot grids, draw line segments with as many different lengths as possible by connecting dots. Label each segment with its length. Use the $\sqrt{\ }$ symbol to express lengths that are not whole numbers. (**Hint:** You will need to draw squares that extend beyond the 5-dot-by-5-dot grids.)

2. List the lengths in increasing order.

3. Estimate each non-whole number length to one decimal place.

B. Ella says the length of the segment at the left below is $\sqrt{8}$ units. Isabel says it is $2\sqrt{2}$ units. Are both students correct? Explain.

C. 1. Question B gives two ways of expressing the exact length of a segment. Express the exact length of the segment at the right above in two ways.

2. Can you find a segment whose length cannot be expressed in two ways as in Question B?

ACE **Homework starts on page 23.**

22 Looking for Pythagoras

Notes

Applications

1. Find the area of every square that can be drawn by connecting dots on a 3 dot-by-3 dot grid.

2. On dot paper, draw a hexagon with an area of 16 square units.

3. On dot paper, draw a square with an area of 2 square units. Write an argument to convince a friend that the area is 2 square units.

4. Consider segment *AB* at right.

    a. On dot paper, draw a square with side *AB*. What is the area of the square?

    b. Use a calculator to estimate the length of segment *AB*.

5. Consider segment *CD* at right.

    a. On dot paper, draw a square with side *CD*. What is the area of the square?

    b. Use a calculator to estimate the length of segment *CD*.

6. Find the area and the side length of this square.

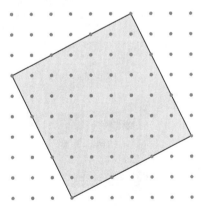

Investigation 2 Squaring Off   **23**

For Exercises 7–34, do not use the $\sqrt{}$ key on your calculator.

For Exercises 7–9, estimate each square root to one decimal place.

7. $\sqrt{11}$ **8.** $\sqrt{30}$ **9.** $\sqrt{172}$

Go Online
PHSchool.com
For: Multiple-Choice Skills
Practice
Web Code: apa-2254

10. Multiple Choice Choose the pair of numbers $\sqrt{15}$ is between.

     A. 3.7 and 3.8   **B.** 3.8 and 3.9   **C.** 3.9 and 4.0   **D.** 14 and 16

Find exact values for each square root.

11. $\sqrt{144}$ **12.** $\sqrt{0.36}$ **13.** $\sqrt{961}$

Find the two consecutive whole numbers the square root is between. Explain.

14. $\sqrt{27}$ **15.** $\sqrt{1,000}$

Tell whether each statement is true.

16. $6 = \sqrt{36}$ **17.** $1.5 = \sqrt{2.25}$ **18.** $11 = \sqrt{101}$

Find the missing number.

19. $\sqrt{\blacksquare} = 81$ **20.** $14 = \sqrt{\blacksquare}$ **21.** $\blacksquare = \sqrt{28.09}$

22. $\sqrt{\blacksquare} = 3.2$ **23.** $\sqrt{\blacksquare} = \frac{1}{4}$ **24.** $\sqrt{\frac{4}{9}} = \blacksquare$

Find each product.

25. $\sqrt{2} \cdot \sqrt{2}$ **26.** $\sqrt{3} \cdot \sqrt{3}$ **27.** $\sqrt{4} \cdot \sqrt{4}$ **28.** $\sqrt{5} \cdot \sqrt{5}$

Give both the positive and negative square roots of each number.

29. 1   **30.** 4   **31.** 2

32. 16   **33.** 25   **34.** 5

Sorry, you can't use my square root key.

Notes _____

_____

_____

_____

35. Find the length of every line segment that can be drawn by connecting dots on a 3 dot-by-3 dot grid.

Homework Help Online
PHSchool.com
For: Help with Exercise 35
Web Code: ape-2235

36. Consider this segment.

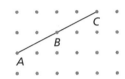

a. Express the exact length of the segment, using the $\sqrt{}$ symbol.

b. What two consecutive whole numbers is the length of the segment between?

37. Show that $2\sqrt{5}$ is equal to $\sqrt{20}$ by finding the length of line segment AC in two ways:

- Find the length of AB. Use the result to find the length of AC.
- Find the length of AC directly, as you did in Problem 2.3.

38. Multiple Choice Which line segment has a length of $\sqrt{17}$ units?

F.

G.

H.

J.

Notes _____

_____

_____

_____

For Exercises 39 and 40, find the length of each side of the figure.

39.

40.

41. Put the following set of numbers in order on a number line.

| 2.3 | $2\frac{1}{4}$ | $\sqrt{5}$ | $\sqrt{2}$ | $\frac{5}{2}$ | $\sqrt{4}$ |

| 4 | -2.3 | $-2\frac{1}{4}$ | $\frac{4}{2}$ | $-\frac{4}{2}$ | 2.09 |

Connections

42. a. Which of the triangles below are right triangles? Explain.

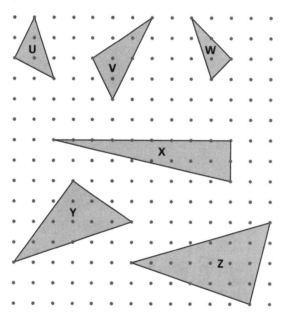

b. Find the area of each right triangle.

Notes _____

_____

_____

_____

43. Refer to the squares you drew in Problem 2.1.

   a. Give the perimeter of each square to the nearest hundredth of a unit.

   b. What rule can you use to calculate the perimeter of a square if you know the length of a side?

44. On grid paper, draw coordinate axes like the ones below. Plot point P at $(1, -2)$.

   a. Draw a square $PQRS$ with an area of 10 square units.

   b. Name a vertex of your square that is $\sqrt{10}$ units from point P.

   c. Give the coordinates of at least two other points that are $\sqrt{10}$ units from point P.

P needs to be a vertex of the square.

Investigation 2 Squaring Off   **27**

Notes _____

_____

_____

_____

45. In Problem 2.3, you drew segments of length 1 unit, $\sqrt{2}$ units, 4 units, and so on. On a copy of the number line below, locate and label each length you drew. On the number line, $\sqrt{1}$ and $\sqrt{2}$ have been marked as examples.

46. In Problem 2.1, it was easier to find the "upright" squares. Two of these squares are represented on the coordinate grid.

   a. Are these squares similar? Explain.

   b. How are the coordinates of the corresponding vertices related?

   c. How are the areas of the squares related?

   d. Copy the drawing. Add two more "upright" squares with a vertex at $(0, 0)$. How are the coordinates of the vertices of these new squares related to the 2×2 square? How are their areas related?

Notes _____

_____

_____

_____

Extensions

47. On dot paper, draw a non-rectangular parallelogram with an area of 6 square units.

48. On dot paper, draw a triangle with an area of 5 square units.

49. Dalida claims that $\sqrt{8} + \sqrt{8}$ is equal to $\sqrt{16}$ because 8 plus 8 is 16. Is she right? Explain.

50. The drawing shows three right triangles with a common side.

    a. Find the length of the common side.

    b. Do the three triangles have the same area? Explain.

We know that $\sqrt{5} \cdot \sqrt{5} = \sqrt{5 \cdot 5} = \sqrt{25} = 5$. Tell whether each product is a whole number. Explain.

51. $\sqrt{2} \cdot \sqrt{50}$

52. $\sqrt{4} \cdot \sqrt{16}$

53. $\sqrt{4} \cdot \sqrt{6}$

Notes _____

_____

_____

_____

Mathematical Reflections 2

In this investigation, you explored squares and segments drawn on dot paper. You learned that the side length of a square is the positive square root of the square's area. You also discovered that, in many cases, a square root is not a whole number. These questions will help you summarize what you have learned.

Think about your answers to these questions. Discuss your ideas with other students and your teacher. Then write a summary of your findings in your notebook.

1. Describe how you would find the length of a line segment connecting two dots on dot paper. Be sure to consider horizontal, vertical, and tilted segments.

2. Explain what it means to find the square root of a number.

Notes

Investigation

ACE Assignment Choices

Differentiated Instruction
Solutions for All Learners

Problem 2.1
Core 1, 2, 42
Other *Applications* 3; *Extensions* 47, 48

Problem 2.2
Core 4–6, 10, 14–18
Other *Applications* 7–9, 11–13, 19–34; unassigned choices from earlier problems

Problem 2.3
Core 35–37, 41
Other *Applications* 38–40; *Connections* 43–46; *Extensions* 49–53; unassigned choices from earlier problems

Adapted For suggestions about adapting Exercise 41 and other ACE exercises, see the CMP *Special Needs Handbook*.
Connecting to Prior Units 42: *Shapes and Designs*; 43: *Covering and Surrounding*; 45: *Bits and Pieces III*; 46: *Stretching and Shrinking*

Applications

1. 1, 2, and 4 units^2

2. Possible answer:

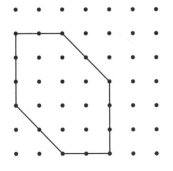

3. Possible answer: By subdividing the square along its diagonals, you get four triangles, each with an area of $\frac{1}{2}$ unit^2. Therefore, the square has an area of 2 units^2.

Note: Ask students to draw the square above inside an upright square with an area of 4 units^2. Then, ask how the larger square can be used to find the area of the smaller square. Because each triangle formed has an area of $\frac{1}{2}$ unit^2, the area of the smaller square is $4 - (4 \cdot \frac{1}{2}) = 2$ units^2.

4. a. 2 units^2 **b.** About 1.414 units

5. a. 5 units^2 **b.** About 2.236 units

6. Area: 45 units^2; side length: $\sqrt{45}$ units, or about 6.708 units

7. $\sqrt{11} \approx 3.3$ **8.** $\sqrt{30} \approx 5.5$

9. $\sqrt{172} \approx 13.1$

10. B   **11.** 12   **12.** 0.6   **13.** 31

14. 5 and 6. Because 27 is between 5^2 and 6^2, $\sqrt{27}$ is between 5 and 6.

15. 31 and 32. Because 1,000 is between 31^2 and 32^2, $\sqrt{1,000}$ is between 31 and 32.

16. True   **17.** True

18. False. $11^2 = 121$

19. 6,561   **20.** 196   **21.** 5.3

22. 10.24   **23.** $\frac{1}{16}$ **24.** $\frac{2}{3}$

25. 2   **26.** 3

27. 4   **28.** 5

29. 1 and –1   **30.** 2 and –2

31. $\sqrt{2}$ and $-\sqrt{2}$ **32.** 4 and –4

33. 5 and –5   **34.** $\sqrt{5}$ and $-\sqrt{5}$

35. 1 unit, $\sqrt{2}$ units, 2 units, $\sqrt{5}$ units, $\sqrt{8}$ units

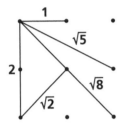

36. a. $\sqrt{29}$ units

b. 5 and 6. 5^2 is 25 and 6^2 is 36, and 29 is between 25 and 36.

37. First way: The area of a square with side AB is 5 units^2. So, the length of AB is $\sqrt{5}$ units. The length of AC is twice the length of AB. So, the length of AC is $2\sqrt{5}$ units.

Second way: The area of a square with side AC is 20 units^2. So, the length of AC is $\sqrt{20}$ units.

38. G

39. $AB = \sqrt{5}$ units; $BC = \sqrt{5}$ units; $CD = \sqrt{2}$ units, $DA = \sqrt{2}$ units

40. $EF = \sqrt{13}$ units; $FG = 1$ unit; $GH = 1$ unit; $HJ = \sqrt{2}$ units; $JK = \sqrt{2}$ units; $KL = \sqrt{5}$ units; $LE = \sqrt{2}$ units

41. (Figure 1)

Connections

42. a. U, W, and X are right triangles. Possible reasoning: I used a corner of a piece of paper (or an angle ruler) to check for 90° angles.

b. Triangle U: 2.5 units^2; Triangle W: 2 units^2, Triangle X: 9 units^2.

43. a.

Area (units^2)	Perimeter (units)
1	4
2	$4\sqrt{2} \approx 5.66$
4	8
5	$4\sqrt{5} \approx 8.94$
8	$4\sqrt{8} \approx 11.31$
9	12
10	$4\sqrt{10} \approx 12.65$
16	16

b. The perimeter is the length of a side multiplied by 4. Symbolically, $P = 4\ell$.

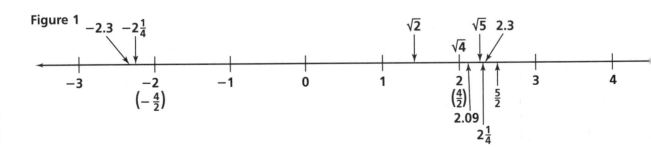

Figure 1

44. a. Possible answer:

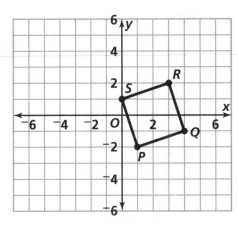

b. Q or S

c. Eight possibilities are shown.

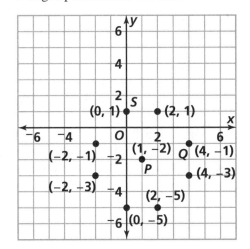

45. (Figure 2)

46. a. Yes. All squares are similar to each other.

b. The coordinates of each vertex of the larger square are twice the coordinates of the corresponding vertex of the smaller square.

c. The area of the larger square is 4 times the area of the smaller square.

d. Squares will vary. However, the coordinates of each vertex of the larger square will be some constant, *a*, times the coordinates of the corresponding vertex of the smaller square. The area of the larger square will be a^2 times the area of the smaller square.

Extensions

47. Possible answers:

48. Possible answers:

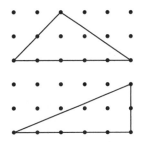

49. No. Possible explanation: $\sqrt{8}$ is greater than 2, so $\sqrt{8} + \sqrt{8}$ is greater than 4. However, $\sqrt{16}$ is 4.

Figure 2

50. a. $\sqrt{10}$

b. No. Possible explanations: The rectangles made from putting together two copies of each triangle have different areas, so the triangles must have different areas.

rectangle area = 4 units²

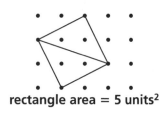

rectangle area = 5 units²

rectangle area = 3 units²

Or, the three triangles have the same base but different heights so they must have different areas.

51. Whole number. $\sqrt{2} \cdot \sqrt{50} = \sqrt{100} = 10$

52. Whole number. $\sqrt{4} \cdot \sqrt{16} = 2 \cdot 4 = 8$ or
$\sqrt{4} \cdot \sqrt{16} = \sqrt{64} = 8$

53. Not a whole number.
$\sqrt{4} \cdot \sqrt{6} = \sqrt{4 \cdot 6} = \sqrt{24} \approx 4.9$

Possible Answers to Mathematical Reflections

1. To find the length of a horizontal or vertical line segment, you can just count the units. To find the length of a diagonal segment, you can draw a square with the segment as a side and then take the square root of the square's area, which gives the length of a side of the square. Or, you might be able to compare the segment to others for which you know the lengths. For example, the longer segment below is twice the length of the shorter segment. The length of the shorter segment is $\sqrt{2}$, so the length of the longer segment is $2 \cdot \sqrt{2}$ or $2\sqrt{2}$.

2. Taking the square root of a number is the opposite of finding the square. For example, if $a \cdot a = 9$, then a is the square root of 9. Every positive number has two square roots. In this case, the square root of 9 is 3 and –3, because $3 \cdot 3 = 9$ and $-3 \cdot -3 = 9$. We can show this by writing $3 = \sqrt{9}$ and $-3 = -\sqrt{9}$.

investigation 3 — The Pythagorean Theorem

Mathematical and Problem-Solving Goals

- Deduce the Pythagorean Theorem through exploration
- Use the Pythagorean Theorem to find unknown side lengths of right triangles
- Reason through a geometric proof of the Pythagorean Theorem
- Use the Pythagorean Theorem to find the distance between two points on a grid
- Determine whether a triangle is a right triangle based on its side lengths
- Relate areas of squares to the lengths of the sides

Summary of Problems

Problem 3.1 **The Pythagorean Theorem**

Students collect information about the areas of the squares on the sides of right triangles and conjecture that the sum of the areas of the two smaller squares equals the area of the largest square.

Problem 3.2 **A Proof of the Pythagorean Theorem**

Students investigate a puzzle that verifies that the sum of the areas of the squares on the legs of a right triangle is equal to the area of the square on the hypotenuse.

Problem 3.3 **Finding Distances**

Students use the Pythagorean Theorem to find distances between dots on a grid.

Problem 3.4 **Measuring the Egyptian Way**

Students explore the converse of the Pythagorean Theorem: If a, b, and c are the lengths of the sides of a triangle and $a^2 + b^2 = c^2$, then the triangle is a right triangle.

Suggested Pacing	Materials for Students	Materials for Teachers	ACE Assignments
6 days	Calculators, centimeter rulers		
2 days	Dot paper	Transparency 3.1	1–14
1 day	Labsheets 3.2A–C, scissors	Transparencies 3.2A, 3.2B	18–23, 26
1 day	Labsheet 3.3	Transparency 3.3	24, 27–35
$1\frac{1}{2}$ days	String; straws or polystrips (optional)	Transparency 3.4	15–17, 25
$\frac{1}{2}$ day			

3.1 The Pythagorean Theorem

Goals

- Deduce the Pythagorean Theorem through exploration

- Use the Pythagorean Theorem to find unknown side lengths of right triangles

In this problem, students collect data about the areas of squares on the sides of a right triangle. They use patterns in their data to conjecture that the sum of the areas of the two smaller squares equals the area of the largest square.

Launch 3.1

To introduce the topic, draw a right triangle below on a dot grid at the board or overhead.

- *What kind of triangle have I drawn?* (A right triangle)

Explain that in a right triangle, the two sides that form the right angle are called the *legs* of the right triangle. The side opposite the right angle is called the *hypotenuse*.

- *What are the lengths of the two legs of this triangle?* (1 unit)

Suggested Questions Ask:

- *How can we find the length of the hypotenuse of the triangle?* (Draw a square using this segment as a side. Then, find the area of the square and take its square root.)

Draw squares on the legs of the triangle.

- *What are the areas of the squares on the legs?* (Both squares have an area of 1 square unit.)

- *What is the area of the square on the hypotenuse?* (2 square units)

Students may notice that the sum of the area of the squares on the legs is equal to the area of the square on the hypotenuse, but don't push for this observation at this time. You might say:

- *In Problem 3.1, you will be looking for a relationship among the three squares that can be drawn on the sides of a right triangle. It will help to organize your work in a table so that you can look for patterns.*

Have students work in groups of three or four.

Explore 3.1

Ask that each student complete a table. Encourage the students in each group to share their work, with each student finding the areas for two or three of the right triangles.

Check to see that students are correctly drawing the squares on the right triangles.

Summarize 3.1

Ask the class to discuss the patterns they see in the table. They should notice that the sum of the areas of the squares on the legs is equal to the area of the square on the hypotenuse.

Suggested Questions Ask:

- *What conjecture can you make about your results?* (When you add the areas of the squares on the legs, you get the area of the square on the hypotenuse.)

- *This pattern is called the Pythagorean Theorem.*

Draw and label a right triangle as shown below.

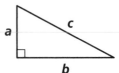

- *Suppose a right triangle has legs of lengths* a *and* b *and a hypotenuse of length* c. *Using these letters, can you state the Pythagorean Theorem in a general way?* (If a and b are the lengths of the legs of a right triangle and c is the length of the hypotenuse, then $a^2 + b^2 = c^2$.)

- *Do you think the Pythagorean Theorem will work for triangles that are not right triangles?*

To help the class explore this question, draw the triangle shown below on the board or overhead (or have the class try this example on their own). Use a corner of a sheet of paper to verify that the triangle does not contain a right angle.

Then, draw squares on each side of the triangle.

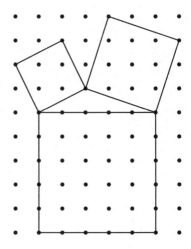

Suggested Questions Ask:

- *We have shown that this triangle is not a right triangle. What are the areas of the squares on its sides?* (5, 10, and 25 square units)

- *Is the sum of the areas of the squares on the shorter sides equal to the area of the square on the longest side?* (No; $5 + 10 \neq 25$)

Next, ask the class this question:

- *Do you think the Pythagorean Theorem is true for all right triangles, even if the sides are not whole numbers?*

The theorem is true for all right triangles. To help the class explore this, you may want to do ACE Exercises 13 and 14 as a class. The triangle in Exercise 14 has leg lengths $\sqrt{5}$ units and $\sqrt{5}$ units, and hypotenuse length $\sqrt{10}$. The squares of these side lengths are 5, 5, and 10 and $5 + 5 = 10$. This shows that the Pythagorean Theorem applies to a right triangle with side lengths that are not whole numbers. A proof that shows the theorem is true for all right triangles is developed in the next problem.

The Pythagorean Theorem is useful for finding unknown side lengths in a right triangle. In this spirit, you could wrap up by having students add a column to their tables, labeled "Length of Hypotenuse." Fill in this column together, or give students a short period of time to complete it themselves and then check the results as a class.

Suggested Question Choose one of the right triangles in the table, list the lengths of the three sides, and ask students what the Pythagorean Theorem says about these lengths.

- *The lengths of the sides of a right triangle are 2, 3, and $\sqrt{13}$. What does the Pythagorean Theorem say about these lengths?* ($2^2 + 3^2 = (\sqrt{13})^2$, or $4 + 9 = 13$)

Repeat the question for lengths 5, 12, and 13.

3.1 The Pythagorean Theorem

Mathematical Goals

- Deduce the Pythagorean Theorem through exploration
- Use the Pythagorean Theorem to find unknown side lengths of right triangles

Launch

Draw a tilted line segment on a dot grid at the board or overhead. Ask:

- *How can we find the length of this line segment?*

Using the original line segment as a hypotenuse, draw two line segments to make a right triangle.

- *What kind of triangle have I drawn?*

Explain that in a right triangle, the two sides that form the right angle are called the *legs* of the right triangle. The side opposite the right angle is called the *hypotenuse.*

- *What are the lengths of the two legs of this triangle?*
- *What are the areas of the squares on the legs? What is the area of the square on the hypotenuse?*

Have students work in groups of three or four on the problem.

Materials
- Dot paper
- Centimeter rulers

Vocabulary
- hypotenuse
- legs

Explore

Ask that each student complete a table. Encourage the students in each group to share the work, with each student finding the areas for two or three of the right triangles.

As you circulate, check to see that students are correctly drawing the squares on the right triangles.

Discuss the patterns in the table.

- *What conjecture can you make about your results? This pattern is called the Pythagorean Theorem.*
- *Suppose a right triangle has legs of lengths* a *and* b *and a hypotenuse of length* c. *Using these letters, can you state the Pythagorean Theorem in a general way?*
- *Do you think the Pythagorean Theorem will work for triangles that are not right triangles?*

Help the class explore this question by drawing a non-right triangle and then drawing squares on the sides. Then ask:

- *Do you think the Pythagorean Theorem is true for all right triangles, even if the sides are not whole numbers?*

The theorem is true for all right triangles. To help the class explore this, you may want to do ACE Exercises 13 and 14 as a class.

Materials
- Transparency 3.1 (optional)

Summarize

You could wrap up by having students add a column to their tables, labeled "Length of Hypotenuse." Fill in this column together, or give students time to complete it themselves and then check the results as a class.

Choose one of the right triangles in the table, list the lengths of the three sides, and ask students what the Pythagorean Theorem says about these lengths.

Materials
- Student notebooks

Vocabulary
- conjecture
- Pythagorean Theorem

ACE Assignment Guide for Problem 3.1

Core 1, 2, 5, 6, 8–11, 12
Other *Applications* 3, 4, 7, 13, 14

Adapted For suggestions about adapting Exercises 8–11 and other ACE exercises, see the CMP *Special Needs Handbook*.
Connecting to Prior Units 18–22: *Filling and Wrapping*

Answers to Problem 3.1

A. (Figure 1)

B. The area of the square on the hypotenuse is equal to the sum of the areas of the squares on the legs.

C. Possible answer: If the legs of a right triangle are 4 units and 1 unit, then the area of the square on the hypotenuse is 17 units^2 because $16 + 1 = 17$.

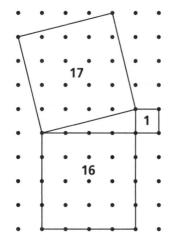

Figure 1

Length of Leg 1 (units)	Length of Leg 2 (units)	Area of Square on Leg 1 (units^2)	Area of Square on Leg 2 (units^2)	Area of Square on Hypotenuse (units^2)
1	1	1	1	2
1	2	1	4	5
2	2	4	4	8
1	3	1	9	10
2	3	4	9	13
3	3	9	9	18
3	4	9	16	25

A Proof of the Pythagorean Theorem

Goal

- Reason through a geometric proof of the Pythagorean Theorem

In this problem, students investigate a puzzle that verifies that the sum of the areas of the squares on the legs of a right triangle is equal to the area of the square on the hypotenuse. Students are again introduced to this idea in symbolic form: If a and b are the lengths of the legs of a right triangle, and c is the length of the hypotenuse, then $a^2 + b^2 = c^2$.

Launch 3.2

We have seen many examples of right triangles that satisfy the Pythagorean Theorem. While these examples are convincing, we can never be sure that this theorem works for <u>all</u> right triangles. To be sure, we need a mathematical proof which uses reasoning to show that a conjecture is always true.

Explain that there are many proofs of the Pythagorean Theorem. One of the proofs is based on the puzzle they will explore in this problem.

Display a set of puzzle pieces on the overhead. Ask students if they see any relationships among the puzzle pieces. Some may notice that the square pieces fit on the sides of the right triangle.

- *I'm handing out sheets containing two puzzle frames and 11 puzzle pieces. Your task is to arrange the puzzle pieces in the two frames using 4 triangles in each frame and to look for a relationship among the areas of the three square pieces.*

Have students work in groups of four on the problem. Give each student scissors and a copy of Labsheets 3.2A.

Explore 3.2

Encourage each group to find more than one way to fit the puzzle pieces into the two frames.

Make sure each group compares their results with those of another group.

Pass out a new set of puzzle pieces (Labsheets 3.2B and 3.2C) for some groups to explore.

Summarize 3.2

When groups have finished the problem, ask about any general patterns they noticed. Some may mention the relationship between the squares and the sides of the right triangle. Others may notice that a side length of a puzzle frame is equal to the sum of the lengths of the two legs of each triangle. Demonstrate these relationships at the overhead.

Have a couple of groups show how they arranged their puzzle pieces. The arrangements may differ slightly, but they all lead to the same conclusion. One arrangement is shown below.

Suggested Questions Ask:

- *What relationship do these completed puzzles suggest?*

- *How do the dimensions of the frame relate to the sides of the triangles?*

- *Can you be sure that the puzzle pieces fit the frame precisely?*

- *Would you be able to use this "arrangement" proof for any right triangle?*

Help students to understand the following argument:

- The areas of the frames are equal.

- Each frame contains four identical right triangles.

- The shapes exactly fit the frame, making straight edges where needed, and matching the "$a + b$" dimensions.

- If the four right triangles are removed from each frame, the area of the shapes remaining in the frames must be equal. That is, the sum of the areas of the squares in one frame must equal the area of the square in the other frame.

Label a diagram of one of the arrangements suggested by the class as shown below.

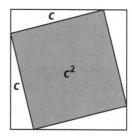

The diagram shows that if the lengths of the legs of a right triangle are a and b and the length of the hypotenuse is c, then $a^2 + b^2 = c^2$.

Suggest that students apply this method to another right triangle (or use Labsheets 3.2B and 3.2C) as part of their homework. They will need to make eleven puzzle pieces and 2 identical frames. Because this procedure will work for any right triangle, this means that our conjecture about the side lengths of a right triangle is true for all right triangles. This is a geometric proof of the Pythagorean Theorem.

Offer an example to help students apply the theorem.

Suggested Question Ask:

- *How can you use the Pythagorean Theorem to find the length of the hypotenuse of a right triangle?* (If we know the lengths of the legs, we can find the areas of the squares on those two sides and add them. This total area is equal to the area of the square on the hypotenuse. Taking the square root of that amount will give us the length of the hypotenuse.)

Check for Understanding

Draw these triangles on the board or overhead:

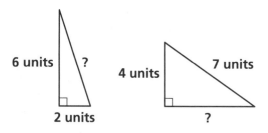

- *How might we find the unknown side lengths in these right triangles?*

Students will likely suggest finding the areas of the squares on the labeled sides. For the triangle on the left, the areas of the squares on the legs are 36 and 4. The sum, 40, is the area of the square on the hypotenuse. The length of the hypotenuse is $\sqrt{40}$. For the triangle on the right, the area of the square on the hypotenuse is 49, which is equal to the sum of the areas of the squares on the legs. The area of the square on the unlabeled leg is thus $49 - 16 = 33$. The missing leg length must be $\sqrt{33}$.

3.2 A Proof of the Pythagorean Theorem

Mathematical Goal

- Reason through a geometric proof of the Pythagorean Theorem

Launch

Explain to the class that there are many proofs of the Pythagorean Theorem. One is based on the puzzle they will explore in this problem.

Display a set of puzzle pieces on the overhead. Ask students if they see any relationships among the puzzle pieces.

- *Your task is to arrange the puzzle pieces in the two frames and to look for a relationship among the areas of the three square pieces.*

Have students work in groups of four on the problem. Give each student scissors and a copy of Labsheet 3.2A.

Materials

- Transparency 3.2A
- Labsheets 3.2A
- Scissors

Explore

Encourage each group to find more than one way to fit the puzzle pieces into the two frames.

Make sure each group compares its results with those of another group.

Pass out a new set of puzzle pieces (Labsheets 3.2B and 3.2C) for some groups to explore.

Materials

- Labsheets 3.2B–C
- Transparency 3.2B

Summarize

When groups have finished the problem, ask about any general patterns they noticed. Demonstrate these relationships at the overhead.

Have groups show how they arranged their puzzle pieces.

- *What relationship do these completed puzzles suggest?*

Help students understand the following argument: The areas of the frames are equal. Each frame contains four identical right triangles. If the four right triangles are removed from each frame, the area remaining in the frames must be equal. That is, the sum of the areas of the squares in one frame must equal the area of the square in the other frame.

Show a diagram of the completed puzzles with sides labeled *a, b,* and *c.* Use the diagram to help students see the symbolic form of the Pythagorean Theorem: $a^2 + b^2 = c^2$. Offer an example to help them apply the theorem.

- *How can you use the Pythagorean Theorem to find the length of the hypotenuse of a right triangle?*

Materials

- Student notebooks

Check for Understanding

Draw two right triangles on the board. One should have legs labeled 6 and 2, and hypotenuse labeled "?". The other should have legs labeled 4 and "?", the hypotenuse labeled 7. Ask students to find the unknown lengths.

ACE Assignment Guide for Problem 3.2

Differentiated Instruction Solutions for All Learners

Core 23, 26

Other *Connections* 18–22, unassigned choices from earlier problems

Adapted For suggestions about adapting ACE exercises, see the CMP *Special Needs Handbook.*
Connecting to Prior Units 23: *Accentuate the Negative*; 26: *Filling and Wrapping*

Answers to Problem 3.2

A. Each side length of the triangle is equal to the lengths of the sides of one of the three squares.

B. 1. Possible arrangement:

2. The sum of the areas of the two smaller squares is equal to the area of the largest square.

3. The sum of the squares of the lengths of the legs of a right triangle is equal to the square of the length of the hypotenuse.

4. Because the procedure for arranging the triangles and squares for this problem can be applied to any right triangle, the conclusion is true for all right triangles.

C. 1. $3^2 + 5^2 = 34 \text{ cm}^2$

2. $\sqrt{34}$ cm, or approximately 5.83 cm

D. For a right triangle with legs of lengths a and b and hypotenuse of length c, $a^2 + b^2 = c^2$.

3.3 Finding Distances

Goals

- Use the Pythagorean Theorem to find the distance between two points on a grid

- Relate areas of squares to the lengths of the sides

In this problem, students discover how the Pythagorean Theorem can be used to find the distance between two dots on a grid.

Launch 3.3

Display Transparency 3.3, or a transparent grid, and indicate or label points K and L as shown in the Student Edition.

Suggested Questions Ask:

- *How can you find the distance between these two points?*

The class may suggest measuring the distance with a ruler. Explain that the Pythagorean Theorem can be used to find an exact length. Draw line segment KL and ask:

- *How can we use the Pythagorean Theorem to find the length of this line segment?*

Some students will probably suggest using the segment as the side of a square; others may suggest using it as the hypotenuse of a right triangle.

- *What right triangle has this hypotenuse?*

Sketch students' suggestions, which may be either of the triangles shown here:

- *What are the lengths of the legs?* (5 units and 2 units)

- *How can you use this information to find the length of the hypotenuse? (The square of the length of the hypotenuse is $5^2 + 2^2$, or 29, so the length is $\sqrt{29}$ units.)*

- *So, what is the distance between points K and L? ($\sqrt{29}$ units)*

Distribute Labsheet 3.3 and have the class work in pairs on the rest of the problem.

Explore 3.3

Students should find the problem a review of what they have learned so far. However, Question D is a bit difficult, so you may need to help guide their thinking.

Suggested Questions Ask:

- *Can the $\sqrt{13}$-unit line segment be a vertical or a horizontal segment?* (No)

- *Why not?* (Vertical and horizontal segments have whole-number lengths on dot grids.)

- *If it is a tilted line segment, can it be the hypotenuse of a right triangle?* (Yes)

- *Assume this segment is the hypotenuse of a right triangle. What will the area of the square on the hypotenuse be?* [$(\sqrt{13})^2$, or 13 square units]

- *What is the sum of the areas of the squares on the legs of this right triangle?* (13)

- *What are two square numbers whose sum is 13?* (4 and 9) *So, what are the lengths of the legs?* ($\sqrt{4}$ units and $\sqrt{9}$ units, or 2 units and 3 units)

Students should draw a right triangle with legs of length 2 units and 3 units. The hypotenuse has length $\sqrt{13}$ units.

Ask students to demonstrate and explain how they found the answers to Questions A–C. Then, go over Question D carefully. After someone has explained how he or she found two points that were $\sqrt{13}$ units apart, offer a similar problem.

- *How would you find a line segment with a length of $\sqrt{40}$ units?*

Ask one or two students to describe their method. They will likely use a guess-and-check procedure to find the two square numbers with a sum of 40, which are 36 and 4. From this they can determine that leg lengths 6 units and 2 units will give a right triangle with a hypotenuse of length $\sqrt{40}$ units. Students should verify their results: $2^2 + 6^2 = 40$, so $\sqrt{40}$ is the length. You can challenge students to find a few more lengths in this way, such as $\sqrt{50}$ units, $\sqrt{61}$ units, and $\sqrt{72}$ units.

If you want your students to have more practice with this idea, you could have them work on ACE Exercises 27–33, either as a final summary activity or as homework after this problem.

Students should be able to focus on the areas of the three squares on the sides of a right triangle and their relationship to the lengths of the sides.

Typically, two lengths or two areas are known, and we must find the third length or area. Once we know the missing area, we can take its square root to find the length. Conversely, once we know the missing length, we can square it to find the area.

The following visual explanation will help some students understand the essence of the Pythagorean Theorem:

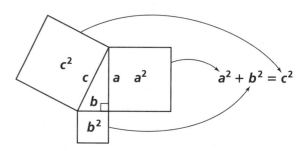

The essential strategy for finding a tilted line with a certain length depends on finding two squares whose sum is equal to the square of that length. In Exercise 27, students create a table of sums of square numbers. This table will help them find the two upright squares whose areas add to the square of the given length. They can use this information to draw a right triangle with the given length as the hypotenuse. As a final check, ask this question:

- *Can 7 be the length of a tilted line segment drawn between two dots on a dot grid?* (No, because 49 does not equal the sum of two square numbers.)

3.3 Finding Distances

Mathematical Goals

- Use the Pythagorean Theorem to find the distance between two points on a grid
- Relate areas of squares to the lengths of the sides

Launch

Display Transparency 3.3, or a transparent grid, and indicate or label points *K* and *L* as shown in the Student Edition.

- *How can you find the distance between these two points?*

Draw line segment *KL* and ask:

- *How can we use the Pythagorean Theorem to find the length of this line segment? What right triangle has this hypotenuse?*

Sketch students' suggestions.

- *What are the lengths of the legs? How can you use this information to find the length of the hypotenuse? So, what is the distance between points K and L?*

Distribute Labsheet 3.3 to each student and have the class work in pairs on the rest of the problem.

Materials
- Transparency 3.3
- Labsheet 3.3

Explore

Students should find the problem a review of what they have learned so far. However, Question D is a bit difficult, so you may need to help guide their thinking.

- *Can the $\sqrt{13}$-unit line segment be a vertical or a horizontal segment?*
- *Assume this segment is the hypotenuse of a right triangle. What will the area of the square of the hypotenuse be?*
- *What is the sum of the areas of the squares on the legs of this right triangle?*
- *What are two square numbers whose sum is 13? So, what are the lengths of the legs?*

Students should draw a right triangle with legs of lengths 2 units and 3 units. The hypotenuse has a length of $\sqrt{13}$ units.

Summarize

Ask students to demonstrate and explain how they found the answers to Questions A–C. Then, go over Question D carefully. Offer a similar problem.

- *How would you find a line segment with a length of $\sqrt{40}$?*

Materials
- Student notebooks

continued on next page

Ask one or two students to describe their method. If you want your students to have more practice with this idea, you could have them work on ACE Exercises 27–33, either as a final summary activity or as homework after this problem.

Students should be able to focus on the areas of the three squares on the sides of a right triangle and their relationship to the lengths of the sides.

ACE Assignment Guide for Problem 3.3

Differentiated Instruction
Solutions for All Learners

Core 24
Other *Extensions* 27–35; unassigned choices from earlier problems

Adapted For suggestions about adapting ACE exercises, see the CMP *Special Needs Handbook*.

Answers to Problem 3.3

A. 1. Two right triangles are possible. In the diagram below, they are *KLW* and *KLV*.

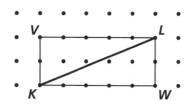

2. 2 and 5

3. $2^2 + 5^2 = 29$, so the length of *KL* is $\sqrt{29}$ units, or about 5.39 units.

B. 5 units. Draw a right triangle with hypotenuse *MN*. Because $3^2 + 4^2 = 25$, the hypotenuse has a length of 5 units.

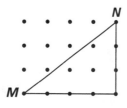

C. $\sqrt{45}$ units, $3\sqrt{5}$ units, or about 6.71 units. Draw a right triangle with hypotenuse *PQ*. Since $3^2 + 6^2 = 45$, the hypotenuse has a length of $\sqrt{45}$ units. This can also be written as $3\sqrt{5}$.

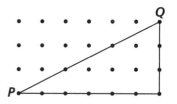

D. Because $(\sqrt{13})^2 = 2^2 + 3^2$, the hypotenuse of a right triangle with legs of lengths 2 units and 3 units will have a length of $\sqrt{13}$ units.

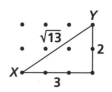

3.4 Measuring the Egyptian Way

Goals

- Determine whether a triangle is a right triangle based on the lengths of its sides
- Relate areas of squares to the lengths of the sides

In this problem, students investigate the converse of the Pythagorean Theorem: If a, b, and c are the lengths of the sides of a triangle and $a^2 + b^2 = c^2$, then the triangle is a right triangle.

Launch 3.4

Discuss the two questions in the introduction to Problem 3.4. Remind students that, so far, they have learned that *if* a triangle is a right triangle, *then* its side lengths satisfy the relationship $a^2 + b^2 = c^2$. However, they do not yet know whether a triangle whose side lengths satisfy this relationship must be a right triangle.

Have students work on the activity in the Getting Ready in pairs. Each pair will need a string, a marker, a ruler, and some tape. The activity is easiest if the strings are cut to lengths that can easily be divided into 12 equal intervals (for example, 48 cm). (If students miscalculate and have string left over, they can just cut off the excess.) Emphasize that students should tape the ends of the string together so there is no overlap.

Suggested Questions After most students have successfully formed a right triangle with whole-number side lengths, discuss the questions.

- *What are the side lengths of the right triangle you formed?* (3 units, 4 units, and 5 units)
- *Do the side lengths satisfy the relationship* $a^2 + b^2 = c^2$? (Yes)
- *How do you think the Egyptians used the knotted rope?* (Possible answer: They formed a triangle with side lengths 3 units, 4 units, and 5 units. This triangle is a right triangle. They used the right angle of the triangle to mark the corners of the rectangular plots.)

Distribute straws, string, or polystrips, and have the class work in pairs on the problem. (**Note:** Students used polystrips in the grade 6 unit *Shapes and Designs* to explore the triangle inequality and to investigate the rigidity of triangles and

quadrilaterals with fixed side lengths. You may be able to borrow them from a sixth-grade teacher. They are a very useful tool for this problem.)

Explore 3.4

If necessary, help students form one of the triangles in Question A so they know what to do.

If you have students who need more practice checking whether three side lengths form a right triangle, you might make up a few examples for them.

Challenge

Ask students to think about the multiples of side lengths of 3-4-5 and 5-12-13, such as 6-8-10 and 10-24-26.

Suggested Questions Ask:

- *Do triangles whose sides have these lengths form a right triangle as well?* (Yes)
- *How do you know?* (Because $6^2 + 8^2 = 10^2$ and $10^2 + 24^2 = 26^2$; because these enlarged triangles are similar to the original triangles, so they have the same angle measure.)

You could also challenge some students to find different sets of whole-number side lengths that make a right triangle. Ask them to explain why.

Summarize 3.4

Have someone demonstrate at the overhead how to arrange the string, straws, or polystrips to form a triangle with side lengths 3 units, 4 units, and 5 units. Ask the student how he or she knows it is a right triangle. Explain that this triangle is sometimes called a "3-4-5 right triangle." Other right triangles are referred to in a similar way.

Suggested Questions Ask:

- *Are multiples of a 3-4-5 triangle, such as 6-8-10 and 9-12-15 triangles, also right triangles?* (Yes, they are all similar triangles, so the measures of corresponding angles are equal. Students might use the language of scale factors or ratios of corresponding sides from their work with the *Stretching and Shrinking* unit to answer this question.)

Have students check these triangles.

$3^2 + 4^2 = 5^2$

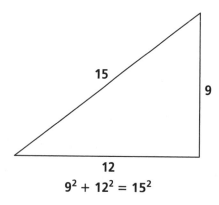

$6^2 + 8^2 = 10^2$

$9^2 + 12^2 = 15^2$

Have students demonstrate each set of lengths on a grid at the overhead, checking for right angles with an angle ruler or a corner of a piece of paper.

• *What about the multiples of 5-12-13? Do these lengths form a right triangle?* (Yes, $10^2 + 24^2 = 26^2$, $15^2 + 36^2 = 39^2$, and so on.)

Tell students that sets of three numbers that satisfy the Pythagorean relationship are called Pythagorean triples. Other whole-number triples are 7-24-25 and 9-40-41.

Spend some time discussing the side lengths that did not form a right triangle.

• *Which of these sets of side lengths did not form a right triangle?* (5, 6, 10; 4, 4, 4; and 1, 2, 2)

• *Does $a^2 + b^2 = c^2$ for these sets?* (No)

• *If the side lengths of a triangle satisfy the condition $a^2 + b^2 = c^2$, is it a right triangle?* (Yes)

• *Can we rearrange the sides of a right triangle to form another triangle that is not a right triangle?* (No; for three given side lengths, there is only one possible triangle. This idea was explored in the grade 6 unit *Shapes and Design*.)

You might want to review students' understanding of the conditions for side lengths of a triangle called the *triangle inequality*, which was explained in *Shapes and Designs*.

• *What about a triangle that has side lengths of 2 units, 6 units, 10 units? Is it a right triangle?* (There is no triangle with these side lengths. These lengths do not satisfy the triangle inequality, which says that the sum of any two side lengths must be greater than the length of the third side length.)

Question B, part (3), asks students if their conjecture will always work. It works for the examples they have tried. Remind students that a few examples are not a proof. A proof for this theorem is given on page 7. You could try to demonstrate this proof or suggest that some students may want to think about a proof (or reasons) for homework.

3.4 Measuring the Egyptian Way

Mathematical Goals

- Determine whether a triangle is a right triangle based on its side lengths
- Relate areas of squares to the lengths of the sides

Launch

Discuss the two questions in the introduction to Problem 3.4. Remind students that, so far, they have learned that *if* a triangle is a right triangle, *then* its side lengths satisfy the relationship $a^2 + b^2 = c^2$. However, they do not yet know whether a triangle whose side lengths satisfy this relationship must be a right triangle.

Have students work on the activity in the Getting Ready in pairs, or do the activity as a demonstration.

Distribute rulers and straws, string, or polystrips, and have the class work in pairs on the problem.

Materials

- Transparency 3.4
- String
- Straws or polystrips
- Centimeter rulers

Explore

If necessary, help students form one of the triangles in Question A.

If you have students who need more practice checking whether three side lengths form a right triangle, you might make up a few examples for them.

Challenge some students to think about the multiples of side lengths of 3-4-5 and 5-12-13, such as 6-8-10 and 10-24-26.

- *Do triangles whose sides have these lengths form a right triangle as well? How do you know?*

You could also challenge some students to find different sets of whole-number side lengths that make a right triangle.

Summarize

Have someone demonstrate how to arrange the string, straws, or polystrips to form a triangle with side lengths 3 units, 4 units, and 5 units and to explain how he or she knows it is a right triangle. Explain that this triangle is sometimes called a "3-4-5 right triangle."

- *Are multiples of a 3-4-5 triangle, such as 6-8-10 and 9-12-15 triangles, also right triangles?*

Have students demonstrate each set of lengths on a grid at the overhead, checking for right angles with an angle ruler or a corner of a piece of paper.

- *What about the multiples of 5-12-13? Do these lengths form a right triangle?*

Also, discuss the side lengths that did not form a right triangle.

- *Which of these sets of side lengths did not form a right triangle? Does $a^2 + b^2 = c^2$ for these sets?*

Materials

- Student notebooks

ACE Assignment Guide
for Problem 3.4

Differentiated
Instruction
Solutions for All Learners

Core 15–17

Other *Connections* 25; unassigned choices from earlier problems

Adapted For suggestions about adapting ACE exercises, see the CMP *Special Needs Handbook*.
Connecting to Prior Units 25: *Filling and Wrapping*

Answers to Problem 3.4

A.

Side Lengths (units)	Do the side lengths satisfy $a^2 + b^2 = c^2$	Is the triangle a right triangle?
3, 4, 5	yes	yes
5, 12, 13	yes	yes
5, 6, 10	no	no
6, 8, 10	yes	yes
4, 4, 4	no	no
1, 2, 2	no	no

B. 1. If a triangle's side lengths satisfy the relationship $a^2 + b^2 = c^2$, the triangle is a right triangle.

  2. If a triangle's side lengths do not satisfy the relationship $a^2 + b^2 = c^2$, the triangle is not a right triangle.

  3. Possible answers: The side lengths 1, 1, and 2 do not satisfy the relationship $a^2 + b^2 = c^2$ and are not lengths of sides of a right triangle. Side lengths 15, 8, and 17 do satisfy $a^2 + b^2 = c^2$ and are side lengths of a right triangle.

C. 1. Yes. $12^2 + 16^2 = 20^2$

  2. Yes. $8^2 + 15^2 = 17^2$

  3. No. $12^2 + 9^2 \neq 16^2$

D. *M*, *N*, *Q*, and *R*. The side lengths of these triangles satisfy the relationship $a^2 + b^2 = c^2$.

Investigation 3

The Pythagorean Theorem

Recall that a right triangle is a triangle with a right, or 90°, angle. The longest side of a right triangle is the side opposite the right angle. We call this side the **hypotenuse** of the triangle. The other two sides are called the **legs.** The right angle of a right triangle is often marked with a square.

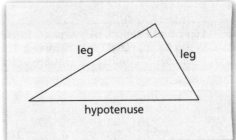

3.1 The Pythagorean Theorem

Each leg of the right triangle on the left below has a length of 1 unit. Suppose you draw squares on the hypotenuse and legs of the triangle, as shown on the right.

How are the areas of the three squares related?

In this problem, you will look for a relationship among the areas of squares drawn on the sides of right triangles.

Investigation 3 The Pythagorean Theorem   **31**

STUDENT PAGE

Notes _____

_____

_____

_____

STUDENT PAGE

A. Copy the table below. For each row of the table:

- Draw a right triangle with the given leg lengths on dot paper.
- Draw a square on each side of the triangle.
- Find the areas of the squares and record the results in the table.

Length of Leg 1 (units)	Length of Leg 2 (units)	Area of Square on Leg 1 (square units)	Area of Square on Leg 2 (square units)	Area of Square on Hypotenuse (square units)
1	1	1	1	2
1	2	■	■	■
2	2	■	■	■
1	3	■	■	■
2	3	■	■	■
3	3	■	■	■
3	4	■	■	■

B. Recall that a **conjecture** is your best guess about a mathematical relationship. It is usually a generalization about a pattern you think might be true, but that you do not yet know for sure is true.

For each triangle, look for a relationship among the areas of the three squares. Make a conjecture about the areas of squares drawn on the sides of any right triangle.

C. Draw a right triangle with side lengths that are different than those given in the table. Use your triangle to test your conjecture from Question B.

ACE Homework starts on page 38.

active math
online

For: Interactive Pythagoras
Visit: PHSchool.com
Web Code: apd-2300

Notes _____

_____

_____

_____

The pattern you discovered in Problem 3.1 is a famous theorem named after the Greek mathematician Pythagoras. A *theorem* is a general mathematical statement that has been proven true. The Pythagorean Theorem is one of the most famous theorems in mathematics.

Over 300 different proofs have been given for the Pythagorean Theorem. One of these proofs is based on the geometric argument you will explore in this problem.

Did You Know?

Pythagoras lived in the sixth century B.C. He had a devoted group of followers known as the Pythagoreans.

The Pythagoreans were a powerful group. Their power and influence became so strong that some people feared they threatened the local political structure, and they were forced to disband. However, many Pythagoreans continued to meet in secret and to teach Pythagoras's ideas.

Because they held Pythagoras in such high regard, the Pythagoreans gave him credit for all of their discoveries. Much of what we now attribute to Pythagoras, including the Pythagorean Theorem, may actually be the work of one or several of his followers.

Go Online
PHSchool.com **For:** Information about Pythagoras **Web Code:** ape-9031

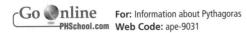

Investigation 3 The Pythagorean Theorem **33**

Notes _____

_____

_____

_____

Problem 3.2 A Proof of the Pythagorean Theorem

Use the puzzles your teacher gives you.

Puzzle frames

Puzzle pieces

A. Study a triangle piece and the three square pieces. How do the side lengths of the squares compare to the side lengths of the triangle?

B. 1. Arrange the 11 puzzle pieces to fit exactly into the two puzzle frames. Use four triangles in each frame.

2. What conclusion can you draw about the relationship among the areas of the three squares?

3. What does the conclusion you reached in part (2) mean in terms of the side lengths of the triangles?

4. Compare your results with those of another group. Did that group come to the same conclusion your group did? Is this conclusion true for all right triangles? Explain.

C. Suppose a right triangle has legs of length 3 centimeters and 5 centimeters.

1. Use your conclusion from Question B to find the area of a square drawn on the hypotenuse of the triangle.

2. What is the length of the hypotenuse?

D. In this Problem and Problem 3.1, you explored the Pythagorean Theorem, a relationship among the side lengths of a right triangle. State this theorem as a rule for any right triangle with leg lengths a and b and hypotenuse length c.

ACE Homework starts on page 38.

34 Looking for Pythagoras

Notes _____

_____

_____

_____

In Investigation 2, you found the lengths of tilted segments by drawing squares and finding their areas. You can also find these lengths using the Pythagorean Theorem.

Problem 3.3 Finding Distances

In Questions A–D, refer to the grid below.

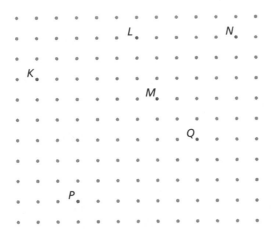

A. 1. Copy the points above onto dot paper. Draw a right triangle with segment KL as its hypotenuse.

2. Find the lengths of the legs of the triangle.

3. Use the Pythagorean Theorem to find the length of segment KL.

B. Find the distance between points M and N by connecting them with a segment and using the method in Question A.

C. Find the distance between points P and Q.

D. Find two points that are $\sqrt{13}$ units apart. Label the points X and Y. Explain how you know the distance between the points is $\sqrt{13}$ units.

ACE Homework starts on page 38.

Notes _____

_____

_____

_____

3.4 Measuring the Egyptian Way

You will now explore these questions about the Pythagorean Theorem:

- Is any triangle whose side lengths a, b, and c, satisfy the relationship $a^2 + b^2 = c^2$ a right triangle?

- Suppose the side lengths of a triangle do *not* satisfy the relationship $a^2 + b^2 = c^2$. Does this mean the triangle is *not* a right triangle?

Getting Ready for Problem 3.4

In ancient Egypt, the Nile River overflowed every year, flooding the surrounding lands and destroying property boundaries. As a result, the Egyptians had to remeasure their land every year.

Because many plots of land were rectangular, the Egyptians needed a reliable way to mark right angles. They devised a clever method involving a rope with equally spaced knots that formed 12 equal intervals.

To understand the Egyptians' method, mark off 12 segments of the same length on a piece of rope or string. Tape the ends of the string together to form a closed loop. Form a right triangle with side lengths that are whole numbers of segments.

- What are the side lengths of the right triangle you formed?
- Do the side lengths satisfy the relationship $a^2 + b^2 = c^2$?
- How do you think the Egyptians used the knotted rope?

Notes _____

_____

_____

_____

A. Copy the table below. Each row gives three side lengths. Use string, straws, or polystrips to build a triangle with the given side lengths. Then, complete the second and third columns of the table.

Side Lengths (units)	Do the side lengths satisfy $a^2 + b^2 = c^2$?	Is the triangle a right triangle?
3, 4, 5		
5, 12, 13		
5, 6, 10		
6, 8, 10		
4, 4, 4		
1, 2, 2		

B. 1. Make a conjecture about triangles whose side lengths satisfy the relationship $a^2 + b^2 = c^2$.

   2. Make a conjecture about triangles whose side lengths do not satisfy the relationship $a^2 + b^2 = c^2$.

   3. Check your conjecture with two other triangles. Explain why your conjecture will always be true.

C. Determine whether the triangle with the given side lengths is a right triangle.

   1. 12 units, 16 units, 20 units

   2. 8 units, 15 units, 17 units

   3. 12 units, 9 units, 16 units

D. Which of these triangles are right triangles? Explain.

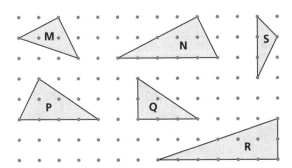

ACE Homework starts on page 38.

Investigation 3 The Pythagorean Theorem   **37**

Notes

Applications

1. A right triangle has legs of length 5 inches and 12 inches.

   a. Find the area of a square drawn on the hypotenuse of the triangle.

   b. What is the length of the hypotenuse?

2. Use the Pythagorean Theorem to find the length of the hypotenuse of this triangle.

Homework
Help Online
PHSchool.com
For: Help with Exercise 2
Web Code: ape-2302

3. On dot paper, find two points that are $\sqrt{17}$ units apart. Label the points W and X. Explain how you know the distance between the points is $\sqrt{17}$ units.

4. On dot paper, find two points that are $\sqrt{20}$ units apart. Label the points Y and Z. Explain how you know the distance between the points is $\sqrt{20}$ units.

Find the missing length(s).

5.

6.

7.

Notes _____

_____

_____

_____

For Exercises 8–11, use the map of Euclid. Find the flying distance in blocks between the two landmarks without using a ruler. Explain.

8. greenhouse and stadium

9. police station and art museum

10. greenhouse and hospital

11. City Hall and gas station

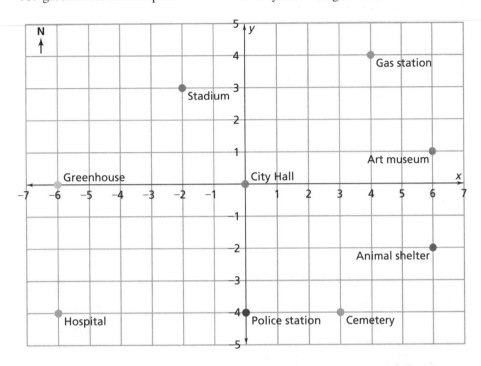

12. Multiple Choice Refer to the map above. Which landmarks are $\sqrt{40}$ blocks apart?

A. greenhouse and stadium

B. City Hall and art museum

C. hospital and art museum

D. animal shelter and police station

Investigation 3 The Pythagorean Theorem   **39**

Notes _____

_____

_____

_____

13. The diagram at the right shows a right triangle with a square on each side.

    a. Find the areas of the three squares.

    b. Use the areas from part (a) to show that this triangle satisfies the Pythagorean Theorem.

14. Show that this triangle satisfies the Pythagorean Theorem.

15. Multiple Choice Choose the set of side lengths that could make a right triangle.

    F. 10 cm, 24 cm, 26 cm   **G.** 4 cm, 6 cm, 10 cm

    H. 5 cm, 10 cm, $\sqrt{50}$ cm   **J.** 8 cm, 9 cm, 15 cm

Tell whether the triangle with the given side lengths is a right triangle.

16. 10 cm, 10 cm, $\sqrt{200}$ cm   **17.** 9 in., 16 in., 25 in.

Go Online
PHSchool.com
For: Multiple-Choice Skills Practice
Web Code: apa-2354

Connections

18. The prism at the right has a base that is a right triangle.

    a. What is the length of a?

    b. Do you need to know the length of a to find the volume of the prism? Do you need to know it to find the surface area? Explain.

    c. What is the volume?

    d. What is the surface area?

    e. Sketch a net for the prism.

Notes _____

_____

_____

_____

For Exercises 19–22, refer to the figures below.

| Cylinder | Cone | Prism | Pyramid |

19. Multiple Choice Which expression represents the volume of the cylinder?

A. $2\pi r^2 + 2\pi rh$ **B.** $\pi r^2 h$ **C.** $\frac{1}{3}\pi r^2 h$ **D.** $\frac{1}{2}\pi r^2 h$

20. Multiple Choice Which expression represents the volume of the cone?

F. $2\pi r^2 + 2\pi rh$ **G.** $\pi r^2 h$ **H.** $\frac{1}{3}\pi r^2 h$ **J.** $\frac{1}{2}\pi r^2 h$

21. Multiple Choice Which expression represents the volume of the prism?

A. $2(\ell w + \ell h + wh)$ **B.** ℓwh

C. $\frac{1}{3}\ell wh$ **D.** $\frac{1}{2}\ell wh$

22. Multiple Choice Which expression represents the volume of the pyramid?

F. $2(\ell w + \ell h + wh)$ **G.** ℓwh

H. $\frac{1}{3}\ell wh$ **J.** $\frac{1}{2}\ell wh$

23. In the city of Euclid, Hilary's house is located at $(5, -3)$, and Jamilla's house is located at $(2, -4)$.

  a. Without plotting points, find the shortest driving distance in blocks between the two houses.

  b. What is the exact flying distance between the two houses?

Investigation 3 The Pythagorean Theorem   **41**

Notes _____

_____

_____

_____

24. Which labeled point is the same distance from point *A* as point *B* is from point *A*? Explain.

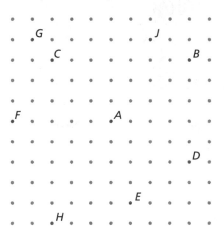

25. In the drawing at right, the cone and the cylinder have the same height and radius. Suppose the radius *r* of the cone is 2 units and the slant height *d* is $\sqrt{29}$ units.

   a. What is the height of the cone?

   b. What is the volume of the cone?

26. In the drawing below, the pyramid and the cube have the same height and base.

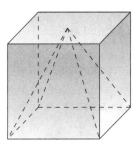

   a. Suppose the edge length of the cube is 6 units. What is the volume of the pyramid?

   b. Suppose the edge length of the cube is *x* units. What is the volume of the pyramid?

Notes _____

_____

_____

_____

Extensions

27. Any tilted segment that connects two dots on dot paper can be the hypotenuse of a right triangle. You can use this idea to draw segments of a given length. The key is finding two square numbers with a sum equal to the square of the length you want to draw.

For example, suppose you want to draw a segment with length $\sqrt{5}$ units. You can draw a right triangle in which the sum of the areas of the squares on the legs is 5. The area of the square on the hypotenuse will be 5 square units, so the length of the hypotenuse will be $\sqrt{5}$ units. Because 1 and 4 are square numbers, and $1 + 4 = 5$, you can draw a right triangle with legs of lengths 1 and 2.

a. To use this method, it helps to be familiar with sums of square numbers. Copy and complete the addition table to show the sums of pairs of square numbers.

+	1	4	9	16	25	36	49	64
1	2	5						
4	5							
9								
16								
25								
36								
49								
64								

For parts (b)–(d) find two square numbers with the given sum.

b. 10   **c.** 25   **d.** 89

For parts (e)–(h), draw tilted segments with the given lengths on dot paper. Use the addition table to help you. Explain your work.

e. $\sqrt{26}$ units   **f.** 10 units

g. $\sqrt{10}$ units   **h.** $\sqrt{50}$ units

Notes _____

_____

_____

_____

For Exercises 28–33, tell whether it is possible to draw a segment of the given length by connecting dots on dot paper. Explain.

28. $\sqrt{2}$ units   **29.** $\sqrt{3}$ units   **30.** $\sqrt{4}$ units

31. $\sqrt{5}$ units   **32.** $\sqrt{6}$ units   **33.** $\sqrt{7}$ units

34. Ryan looks at the diagram below. He says, "If the center of this circle is at the origin, then I can figure out the radius."

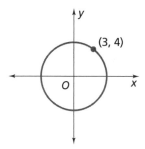

a. Explain how Ryan can find the radius.

b. What is the radius?

35. Use the graph to answer parts (a)–(c).

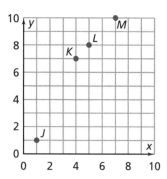

a. Find the coordinates of J and K.

b. Use the coordinates to find the distance from J to K. Explain your method.

c. Use your method from part (b) to find the distance from L to M.

Notes _____

_____

_____

_____

Mathematical Reflections 3

In this investigation, you worked with a very important mathematical relationship called the Pythagorean Theorem. These questions will help you summarize what you have learned.

Think about your answers to these questions. Discuss your ideas with other students and your teacher. Then write a summary of your findings in your notebook.

1. Suppose you are given the lengths of two sides of a right triangle. Describe how you can find the length of the third side.

2. Suppose two points on a grid are not on the same horizontal or vertical line. Describe how you can use the Pythagorean Theorem to find the distance between the points without measuring.

3. How can you determine whether a triangle is a right triangle if you know only the lengths of its sides?

Notes

Investigation 3

ACE
Assignment Choices

Problem 3.1
Core 1, 2, 5, 6, 8–12
Other *Applications* 3, 4, 7, 13, 14

Problem 3.2
Core 23, 26
Other *Connections* 18–22; unassigned choices from earlier problems

Problem 3.3
Core 24
Other *Applications* 27–35; unassigned choices from earlier problems

Problem 3.4
Core 15–17
Other *Connections* 25; unassigned choices from earlier problems

Adapted For suggestions about adapting Exercises 8–11 and other ACE exercises, see the CMP *Special Needs Handbook*.
Connecting to Prior Units 18–22, 25, 26: *Filling and Wrapping*; 23: *Accentuate the Negative*

Applications

1. **a.** $5^2 + 12^2 = 169$ in.^{2}

   b. 13 in.

2. $c^2 = 3^2 + 6^2 = 45$, $c = \sqrt{45}$ cm, or about 6.7 cm.

3. WX is the hypotenuse of a right triangle with legs of length 4 units and 1 unit. Because $4^2 + 1^2 = 17$, the length of segment WX is $\sqrt{17}$ units. Therefore, W and X are $\sqrt{17}$ units apart.

4. *YZ* is the hypotenuse of a right triangle with legs of length 4 units and 2 unit. Because $4^2 + 2^2 = 20$, the length of segment *YZ* is $\sqrt{20}$ units. Therefore, the distance between *Y* and *Z* is $\sqrt{20}$ units.

Note: There are many triangles with a hypotenuse length of $\sqrt{20}$ units (for example, one with legs 3 and $\sqrt{11}$). However, in this case, we want to use integer lengths so we can draw the triangle on dot paper.

5. $h^2 = 4^2 + 3^2 = 25$, so $h = \sqrt{25}$ in. = 5 in.

6. $k^2 = 3^2 + 8^2 = 73$, so $k = \sqrt{73}$ cm ≈ 8.5 cm.

7. $x^2 = 7^2 - 4^2 = 33$, so $x = \sqrt{33}$ m ≈ 5.7 m.
   $y^2 = 21^2 - 4^2 = 425$, so $y = \sqrt{425}$ m ≈ 20.6 m.

8. Because $4^2 + 3^2 = 25$, the distance is 5 blocks.

9. Because $6^2 + 5^2 = 61$, the distance is $\sqrt{61}$ blocks ≈ 7.8 blocks.

10. The distance is 4 blocks.

11. Because $4^2 + 4^2 = 32$, the distance is $\sqrt{32} \approx 5.7$ blocks.

12. D

13. **a.** 2 units, 2 units, 4 units

    b. The side lengths are $\sqrt{2}$ units, $\sqrt{2}$ units, and 2 units, and $(\sqrt{2})^2 + (\sqrt{2})^2 = 2^2$ (that is, $2 + 2 = 4$), so the side lengths satisfy the Pythagorean Theorem.

14. The sides have lengths $\sqrt{5}$ units, $\sqrt{5}$ units, and $\sqrt{10}$ units and, because $(\sqrt{5})^2 + (\sqrt{5})^2 = (\sqrt{10})^2$ (that is, $5 + 5 = 10$), the triangle satisfies the Pythagorean Theorem.

Note: This is a nice place to remind students that $\sqrt{5} + \sqrt{5} \neq \sqrt{10}$, even though $(\sqrt{5})^2 + (\sqrt{5})^2 = (\sqrt{10})^2$. They can use the diagram to show $\sqrt{5} + \sqrt{5} > \sqrt{10}$ or they can use estimation.

15. F

16. This is a right triangle. $10^2 + 10^2 = (\sqrt{200})^2$

17. This is not a right triangle. $9^2 + 16^2 \neq 25^2$.

> **For the Teacher** In fact, these side lengths will not form a triangle of any kind. As in Exercise 16, watch for students who incorrectly write that $\sqrt{9} + \sqrt{16} = \sqrt{25}$.

Connections

18. a. 6.5 cm

b. You do not need to know the value of a to find the volume, but it is needed to find the surface area. To find the volume, you multiply 4 by the area of the triangular face, which you can find using only the given base and height. To find the surface area, you need to find the areas of the rectangular faces. For one of these faces, you need to know the value of a.

c. 30 cm³; $0.5(6 \cdot 2.5) \cdot 4 = 30$

d. 75 cm²; $(2.5 \cdot 4) + 2[0.5(6 \cdot 2.5)] + (6 \cdot 4) + (6.5 \cdot 4) = 10 + 15 + 24 + 26 = 75$

e. Possible sketch:

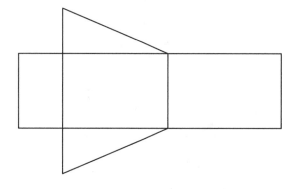

19. B **20.** H **21.** B **22.** H

23. a. 4 blocks

b. $\sqrt{10}$ blocks. Find the length of the segment connecting the points. It is the hypotenuse of a right triangle with leg lengths 1 and 3. The leg lengths are the vertical and horizontal distances between the two points [$(5 - 2)$ units and $-3 - (-4)$ units] $3^2 + 1^2 = 10$, so the distance is $\sqrt{10}$ blocks.

24. Points A and B are 5 units apart. Point F is also 5 units from point A.

25. a. Using the Pythagorean Theorem, $2^2 + h^2 = 29$, so the height h of the cone is 5 units.

b. The volume of the cylinder is $\pi(2)^2(5) = 20\pi$ units³. So the volume of the cone is $\frac{20\pi}{3}$ units³, or about 20.94 units³.

26. a. 72 cubic units. The volume of the cube is $6 \cdot 6 \cdot 6 = 216$ units³. The volume of the pyramid is $\frac{1}{3}$ of the cube's volume, or 72 units³.

b. $\frac{1}{3}x^3$. The cube has volume x^3. The volume of this pyramid is one-third the volume of the cube, so it is $\frac{1}{3}x^3$.

Extensions

27. a. (Figure 2)

b. i. 1 and 9

c. 9 and 16

d. 25 and 64

e. 1 + 25 = 26, so a triangle with leg lengths of 1 unit and 5 units has a hypotenuse of length $\sqrt{26}$ units.

f. 36 + 64 = 100, so a triangle with leg lengths of 6 units and 8 units has a hypotenuse of length 10 units.

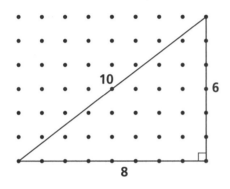

g. 9 + 1 = 10, so a triangle with leg lengths of 3 units and 1 unit has a hypotenuse of length $\sqrt{10}$ units.

h. 49 + 1 = 50, so a triangle with leg lengths of 7 units and 1 unit has a hypotenuse of length $\sqrt{50}$ units.

28. Yes. $\sqrt{2}$ units is the length of the hypotenuse of a right triangle with leg lengths of 1 unit.

29. No. 3 is not the sum of two square numbers.

30. Yes. $\sqrt{4} = 2$, so just draw a horizontal or vertical segment with length 2 units.

31. Yes. $\sqrt{5}$ units is the length of the hypotenuse of a right triangle with leg lengths of 2 units and 1 unit.

32. No. 6 is not the sum of two square numbers.

33. No. 7 is not the sum of two square numbers.

34. a. Possible answer: Draw a right triangle as shown below, and use the Pythagorean Theorem to find the hypotenuse, which is the radius.

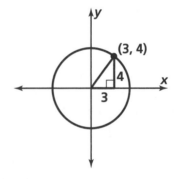

b. 5 units

Figure 2

+	1	4	9	16	25	36	49	64
1	2	5	10	17	26	37	50	65
4	5	8	13	20	29	40	53	68
9	10	13	18	25	34	45	58	73
16	17	20	25	32	41	52	65	80
25	26	29	34	41	50	61	74	89
36	37	40	45	52	61	72	85	100
49	50	53	58	65	74	85	98	113
64	65	68	73	80	89	100	113	128

35. a. $J(1, 1)$; $K(4, 7)$

    b. About 6.7 units. You can draw a right triangle with hypotenuse JK. The length of one leg is the positive difference of the x-coordinates, which is $4 - 1$, or 3. The length of the other leg is the positive difference of the y-coordinates, which is $7 - 1 = 6$. So the length of JK is $\sqrt{9 + 36} = \sqrt{45} \approx 6.7$ units.

    Note: In high school, students will see the distance formula,

$$d = \sqrt{(x_2 - x_1)^2 + (y_2 - y_1)^2},$$

or $d^2 = (x_2 - x_1)^2 + (y_2 - y_1)^2$. The distance formula follows directly from the Pythagorean Theorem. If you use the segment between two points as the hypotenuse of a right triangle, the length of the horizontal leg will be $|x_2 - x_1|$ and the length of the vertical side will be $|y_2 - y_1|$, so the distance between the points, which is the length of the hypotenuse, is $\sqrt{(x_2 - x_1)^2 + (y_2 - y_1)^2}$.

    c. 2.8 units. $\sqrt{(7 - 5)^2 + (10 - 8)^2} = \sqrt{4 + 4} = \sqrt{8} \approx 2.8$

Note: You can give additional extension problems to interested students. For example, you might ask students to find the length of a diagonal of a square with side length a. Or, you could ask them to draw a square of side a inscribed in a circle and then to find the radius and area of the circle in terms of a.

Possible Answers to Mathematical Reflections

1. If we know the lengths of the legs, the length of the hypotenuse can be found by taking the square root of the sum of the squares of the leg lengths. If we know the lengths of one leg and the hypotenuse, we can find the length of the other leg by subtracting the square of the given leg length from the square of the hypotenuse length; this is the square of the missing leg length. Take the square root of that difference to get the missing leg length.

2. Think of the segment between the two points as the hypotenuse of a right triangle. Find the lengths of the legs of the right triangle (which lie on a vertical line and a horizontal line). Apply the Pythagorean Theorem by adding the squares of these two lengths and taking the square root of that sum.

3. Check whether the side lengths satisfy the relationship $a^2 + b^2 = c^2$, where a and b are the lengths of the shorter sides, and c is the length of the longest side. If they do, then the triangle is a right triangle.

Investigation 4 Using the Pythagorean Theorem

Mathematical and Problem-Solving Goals

- Learn the meanings of *rational number* and *irrational number*
- Estimate the values of square roots that are irrational numbers
- Estimate lengths of hypotenuses of right triangles
- Apply the Pythagorean Theorem to a problem situation
- Investigate the special properties of equilateral and 30-60-90 triangles
- Use the properties of special right triangles to solve problems

Summary of Problems

Problem 4.1 Analyzing the Wheel of Theodorus

Students apply the Pythagorean Theorem to find the exact lengths of hypotenuses of right triangles. Then, they use a number-line ruler to estimate the lengths. Finally, they compare their ruler estimates to those made with a calculator.

Problem 4.2 Stopping Sneaky Sally

Students apply the Pythagorean Theorem to find distances on a baseball diamond.

Problem 4.3 Analyzing Triangles

Students investigate properties of equilateral and 30-60-90 triangles by applying the Pythagorean Theorem.

Problem 4.4 Finding the Perimeter

Students draw from their experiences in the previous three problems to find missing lengths and angles in a triangle made up of other triangles.

	Suggested Pacing	Materials for Students	Materials for Teachers	ACE Assignments
All	5 days	Centimeter rulers, student notebooks		
4.1	1 day	Labsheet 4.1, scissors	Transparencies 4.1A and 4.1B	1, 2, 13–16
4.2	1 day		Transparency 4.2	3–9, 17–25, 36–46
4.3	$1\frac{1}{2}$ days		Transparencies 4.3A and 4.3B	10, 11, 26–34, 47–52
4.4	1 day	Labsheet 4.4, scissors	Transparency 4.4	12, 35, 53–58
MR	$\frac{1}{2}$ day			

Analyzing the Wheel of Theodorus

Goals

- Learn the meanings of *rational number* and *irrational number*
- Estimate the values of square roots that are irrational numbers
- Estimate lengths of hypotenuses of right triangles

In this problem, students explore an intriguing pattern of triangles called the *Wheel of Theodorus*. In this series of right triangles, the hypotenuse of one triangle is the longer leg of the next triangle. Students apply the Pythagorean Theorem to find the length of the hypotenuse of each triangle in the wheel. Then, they estimate the hypotenuse lengths with both a number-line ruler and a calculator.

Launch 4.1

Introduce the problem by discussing how to find a decimal approximation for a square root.

- *Think back to when we found the side lengths of tilted squares.*
- *The side length of a square with an area of 2 square units is $\sqrt{2}$ units, the positive number you can multiply by itself to get 2. We estimated this value first by measuring and then by using the $\sqrt{}$ key on a calculator.*
- *Just how large is $\sqrt{2}$? Can you find a decimal number that is equal to $\sqrt{2}$? Where is $\sqrt{2}$ on the number line?*

Draw a simple number line on the board and ask students where $\sqrt{2}$ should be placed.

To answer this, students will have to consider where 1.4 and 1.5 are on the number line. Encourage them to briefly discuss the difficulty of placing a number on a number line when the number cannot be written as an exact decimal. Specifically, you know what decimals it is between, but not exactly where it is in that interval. For example, is it closer to 1.4 or 1.5?

On a dot grid, draw a square with an area of 2 square units on a number line as shown below.

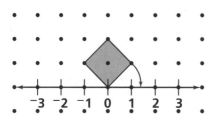

Suggested Questions Ask:

- *What is the length of a side of this square?* ($\sqrt{2}$)
- *If we mark off a segment on the number line with the same length as the side, where will the segment end?* (At about 1.4)

Mark off the length of the segment on the edge of a sheet of paper and transfer it to the number line.

- *So, $\sqrt{2}$ is approximately equal to 1.4. Is 1.4 exactly equal to $\sqrt{2}$?* (No, because $1.4^2 = 1.96$.)
- *Suppose we try 1.41. Does $1.41 = \sqrt{2}$?* (No, it is too small; $1.41^2 = 1.9881$.)
- *Try 1.42. Does it equal $\sqrt{2}$?* (No, it is too large; $1.42^2 = 2.0164$.)
- *Can you find a number that is closer to $\sqrt{2}$ than 1.41 and 1.42 are?*

Students should try numbers between 1.41 and 1.42, such as 1.415, 1.413, and 1.414.

Display the Wheel of Theodorus, which is on Transparency 4.1A. Discuss with the class how the wheel was constructed and ask for the lengths of the second and third hypotenuses. Cut out the number-line ruler and demonstrate how to transfer these lengths to the ruler.

Distribute Labsheet 4.1 and scissors to each student. Have students work in groups of two to four on the problem.

Explore 4.1

Ask that each student label his or her own number-line ruler. As students work, check on their understanding of measuring lengths and writing decimals.

Summarize 4.1

Display the Wheel of Theodorus. Ask for the lengths of the hypotenuses and write them on the wheel. Then, have students come to the front and mark the length of each hypotenuse on the number-line ruler.

Ask for approximations to the nearest tenth for each length. As a class, check each approximation by squaring it on a calculator.

Suggested Question Ask:

- *Is this estimate too large? Is it too small? What might be a better estimate? How do you know?*

Students should square each decimal estimate and compare the result to the square of the length of the hypotenuse. Take this opportunity to assess students' understanding of the ordering of decimals. Students sometimes need to review and practice comparing such numbers as 1.41, 1.415, and 1.42.

Ask students to compare their ruler estimates to the estimates they obtained with a calculator. Calculators display varying numbers of decimal places, but students are usually convinced that, no matter what decimal number their calculators display for $\sqrt{2}$, they have not found an exact decimal equivalent. (Note: On many calculators, if the approximation is not cleared before it is squared, the calculator will display the original square as the answer.)

Discuss the Did You Know? that appears after the problem. Tell students that numbers like $\sqrt{2}$, $\sqrt{7}$, and π are called irrational numbers. They cannot be written as the ratio of two whole numbers. The set of irrational and rational numbers is called the real numbers.

Mathematics Background

For background on real numbers, see page 9.

Mathematical Goals

- Learn the meanings of *rational number* and *irrational number*
- Estimate the values of square roots that are irrational numbers
- Estimate lengths of hypotenuses of right triangles

Launch

Introduce the problem by discussing how to find a decimal approximation for a square root.

On a dot grid, draw a square with an area of 2 square units on a number line, with the "bottom vertex" at point 0.

- *What is the length of a side of this square? If we mark off a segment on the number line with the same length as the side, where will the segment end?*

- *So, $\sqrt{2}$ is approximately equal to 1.4. Is 1.4 exactly equal to $\sqrt{2}$? Suppose we try 1.41. Does 1.41 = $\sqrt{2}$? Try 1.42. Does it equal $\sqrt{2}$? Can you find a number that is closer to $\sqrt{2}$ than 1.41 and 1.42 are?*

Display the Wheel of Theodorus. Explore with the class how the wheel was constructed and ask for the lengths of the second and third hypotenuses. Cut out the number-line ruler and demonstrate how to transfer these lengths to the ruler.

Distribute Labsheet 4.1 and scissors to each student and have students work in groups of two to four on the problem.

Materials

- Transparency 4.1A
- Labsheet 4.1
- Scissors

Explore

Ask that each student label his or her own number-line ruler. Check on students' understanding of measuring lengths and writing decimals.

Summarize

Display the Wheel of Theodorus. Ask for the lengths of the hypotenuses and write them on the wheel. Then, have students come to the front and mark the length of each hypotenuse on the number-line ruler.

Ask for approximations to the nearest tenth for each length. As a class, check each approximation by squaring it on a calculator.

- *Is this estimate too large? Too small? What might be a better estimate? How do you know?*

Take this opportunity to assess students' understanding of the ordering of decimals.

Ask students to compare their estimates to the numbers they obtained with a calculator. Tell the class that the numbers $\sqrt{2}, \sqrt{3}, \sqrt{5}, \ldots$ are called irrational numbers.

Materials

- Student notebooks

Vocabulary

- irrational number

ACE Assignment Guide for Problem 4.1

Core 1, 2
Other *Connections* 13–16

Adapted For suggestions about adapting ACE exercises, see the CMP *Special Needs Handbook*.

Answers to Problem 4.1

A. The lengths of the hypotenuses (in units), from least to greatest, are $\sqrt{2}, \sqrt{3}, 2$ (or $\sqrt{4}$), $\sqrt{5}, \sqrt{6}, \sqrt{7}, \sqrt{8}, 3$ (or $\sqrt{9}$), $\sqrt{10}, \sqrt{11}$, and $\sqrt{12}$.

B. (Figure 1) **Note:** $\sqrt{4} = 2$ and $\sqrt{9} = 3$.

C. 1. $\sqrt{2}$ and $\sqrt{3}$ are between 1 and 2; $\sqrt{5}, \sqrt{6}, \sqrt{7}$, and $\sqrt{8}$ are between 2 and 3; and $\sqrt{10}, \sqrt{11}$, and $\sqrt{12}$ are between 3 and 4.

2. $\sqrt{2}$ is between 1.4 and 1.5; $\sqrt{3}$ is between 1.7 and 1.8; $\sqrt{5}$ is between 2.2 and 2.3; $\sqrt{6}$ is between 2.4 and 2.5; $\sqrt{7}$ is between 2.6 and 2.7; $\sqrt{8}$ is between 2.8 and 2.9; $\sqrt{10}$ is between 3.1 and 3.2; $\sqrt{11}$ is between 3.3 and 3.4; $\sqrt{12}$ is between 3.4 and 3.5.

3. $\sqrt{2} \approx 1.414213562, \sqrt{3} \approx 1.732050808,$ $\sqrt{4} \approx 2, \sqrt{5} \approx 2.236067978,$ $\sqrt{6} \approx 2.449489743, \sqrt{7} \approx 2.645751311,$ $\sqrt{8} \approx 2.828427125, \sqrt{10} \approx 3.16227766,$ $\sqrt{11} \approx 3.31662479, \sqrt{12} \approx 3.464101615.$

The numbers obtained using the ruler and the calculator are both approximations, but the calculator gives greater accuracy.

D. Both students have a valid point. Odakota's number is an estimate accurate to nine decimal places (although most calculators store 13 digits), while Geeta is correct in pointing out that the square of this decimal approximation does not equal exactly 3. (**Note:** It would be impossible to write all the decimal places in the decimal expansion for $\sqrt{3}$.)

Figure 1

Stopping Sneaky Sally

Goals

- Estimate lengths of hypotenuses of right triangles
- Apply the Pythagorean Theorem to a problem situation

In this problem, students apply the Pythagorean Theorem to determine distances on a baseball diamond.

Launch 4.2

Introduce the baseball scenerio described in the student edition. Talk about the layout of a baseball diamond, which is pictured on Transparency 4.2. The baseball diamond is a square.

Suggested Questions Ask:

- *Does anyone know the distance between bases on a standard baseball field?* (90 ft)
- *How far do you think a catcher would need to throw the ball to get a runner out at second base?*

Let students offer a few estimates, and then have them work in pairs on the problem.

Explore 4.2

Suggested Questions Some students may need help in recognizing the right triangles that are the key to solving the problem.

- *Suppose you draw a line segment from home plate to second base. What is special about the line segment?* (It is the hypotenuse of a right triangle whose legs are the segments from home plate to first base and from first base to second base.)

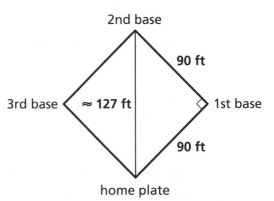

- *What do you know about the side lengths of this right triangle?* (The legs each have a length of 90 ft.)
- *How can you find the length of the hypotenuse?* (You can use the Pythagorean Theorem.)

Repeat these questions, if necessary, for Question B. The line segment from home plate to the point halfway between second and third base is the hypotenuse of a right triangle whose legs are the segments from home plate to third base and from third base to the halfway point between second and third base.

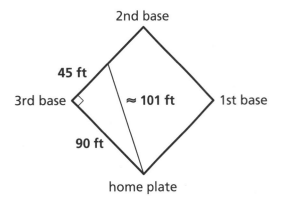

Summarize 4.2

Have several students share their strategies for solving the problem. Look for specific references to the Pythagorean Theorem.

There are a couple of common misconceptions that may arise during this discussion. First, students may add the lengths of the legs and then square the sum to find the square of the hypotenuse. If this happens, you may need to demonstrate with actual numbers that $(a + b)^2 \neq a^2 + b^2$:

$$(90 + 90)^2 \stackrel{?}{=} 90^2 + 90^2$$
$$180^2 \stackrel{?}{=} 90^2 + 90^2$$
$$32{,}400 \stackrel{?}{=} 8{,}100 + 8{,}100$$
$$32{,}400 \neq 16{,}200$$

INVESTIGATION 4

A second misconception involves taking square roots: some students will try to find the length of the hypotenuse by calculating $\sqrt{a^2} + \sqrt{b^2}$ rather than $\sqrt{a^2 + b^2}$. Again, offer numerical examples to help students understand that these expressions are not equivalent. Stress the correct procedure: Students should square each leg length first, add the squares, and then take the square root of the sum. For some students, the symbolic expression, $\sqrt{a^2 + b^2}$, will be an aid to memory. For some, it may be confusing.

4.2 Stopping Sneaky Sally

Mathematical Goals

- Estimate lengths of hypotenuses of right triangles
- Apply the Pythagorean Theorem to a problem situation

Launch

Introduce the baseball scenario described in the Student Edition. Talk about the layout of a baseball diamond, which is pictured on Transparency 4.2. The baseball diamond is a square.

- *Does anyone know the distance between bases on a standard baseball field?*
- *How far do you think a catcher would need to throw the ball to get a runner out at second base?*

Let students offer a few estimates, and then have them work in pairs on the problem.

Materials

- Transparency 4.2

Explore

Some students may need help in recognizing the right triangles that are the key to solving the problem.

- *Suppose you draw a line segment from home plate to second base. What is special about the line segment?*
- *What do you know about the side lengths of this right triangle? How can you find the length of the hypotenuse?*

Repeat these questions, if necessary, for Question B.

Summarize

Have several students share their strategies for solving the problem. Look for specific references to the Pythagorean Theorem.

Stress the correct procedure: Square each leg length first, add the squares, and then take the square root of the sum to get the length of the hypotenuse.

Materials

- Student notebooks

ACE Assignment Guide for Problem 4.2

Differentiated Instruction Solutions for All Learners

Core 3–5, 24, 25
Other *Applications* 6–9; *Connections* 17–23, 36, 37; *Extensions* 38–46; unassigned choices from earlier problems

Adapted For suggestions about adapting Exercise 8 and other ACE exercises, see the CMP *Special Needs Handbook*.
Connecting to Prior Units 17–18: *Moving Straight Ahead*

Answers to Problem 4.2

A. Because $90^2 + 90^2 = 16{,}200$, the distance from home plate to second base is $\sqrt{16{,}200}$ ft, or about, 127.28 ft.

B. The shortstop is standing on the baseline at a distance of $90 \div 2 = 45$ ft from third base. Because $90^2 + 45^2 = 10{,}125$, the distance from home plate to the shortstop is $\sqrt{10{,}125}$ ft, or about 100.62 ft.

C. The pitcher's mound is not exactly halfway between home plate and second base. The distance from the pitcher's mound to second base is $127.28 - 60.5 \approx 66.78$ ft.

To find the distance to first base, you need to find the halfway point between home and second base, which is about $127.28 \div 2$, or about 63.64 ft from home plate. Then, draw a right triangle with vertices at the halfway point, the pitcher's mound, and first base.

halfway point between home plate and 2nd base
63.64 ft
3.14 ft — 1st base
pitcher's mound

The lengths of the legs are 63.64 ft and 3.14 ft. (3.14 ft is the distance between the pitcher's mound and the halfway point between home plate and second base. 63.64 ft is half of the distance between first and third bases, which is the same as the distance between home plate and second base.)

Use the Pythagorean Theorem to find the distance between the pitcher's mound and first base:
$\sqrt{(3.14)^2 + (63.64)^2} \approx 63.72$ ft. The distance between the pitcher's mound and third base is also about 63.72 ft.

Analyzing Triangles

Goal

- Investigate the special properties of a 30-60-90 triangle

Launch 4.3

Show a transparency of the Getting Ready for Problem 4.3.

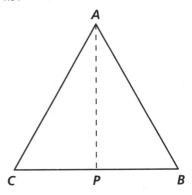

Suggested Questions Ask:

- *This is an equilateral triangle. What is true about the lengths of the sides of an equilateral triangle?* (They are all equal.)

- *What is true about the sum of the angles in any triangle?* (It is 180°.)

- *What is true about the measures of the angles of an equilateral triangle?* (They are all equal.)

- *What is the measure of each angle in an equilateral triangle?* (The sum of the angles in any triangle is 180°, so each angle must measure 60°.)

Tell the class that *AP* is a reflection line of symmetry.

- *What is a reflection line of symmetry? (It is a line that divides a triangle into two identical shapes.)*

Some students may need to be reminded about reflection line symmetries. Cut out a copy of triangle *ABC* and fold it along the reflection line. Ask the students what they observe about the two shapes (smaller triangles) that are created. Students should discover that line segment *AP* divides triangle *ABC* into two congruent triangles. You may

want to remind students that triangles are congruent if each pair of corresponding sides has the same length. More informally, in one triangle fits on another triangle exactly, or if two triangles have the same size and shape, they are congruent.

- *What can you say about the measures of angles CAP, BAP, CPA, and BPA?* (Angles *CAP* and *BAP* are equal. So each has a measure of 30°. Angles *CPA* and *BPA* are also equal. Since the two angles form a straight angle and they are equal, they must each be 90°.)

- *What can you say about line segments CP and PB?* (These segments have equal lengths or each of them is half of the length of a side of the equilateral triangle.)

- *What can you say about triangles ACP and ABP?* (The triangles are congruent or have identical shapes. Each is a right triangle.)

Label the angles of the triangle as 30, 60, and 90 degrees. Students can work in pairs on the problem.

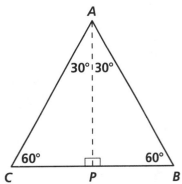

- *We have just explored some interesting relationships in an equilateral triangle that occur when a line of reflection is drawn. In Problem 4.3, you will continue to explore these relationships about angles and side lengths.*

Explore 4.3

If students are having trouble, ask questions to help them see that two right triangles were formed by the line of symmetry. Then, ask what else they know about these right triangles.

Make sure students are determining the side lengths by using the Pythagorean Theorem, not by measuring.

Summarize 4.3

Let several pairs share their reasoning about each question, demonstrating their work at the board or overhead.

For Question A, students should be able to reason that both triangles have angles of measure 30°, 60°, and 90°. The reflection line (also called the median or midpoint line) forms two congruent angles along the base of the original equilateral triangle. As the sum of the angles along a straight line is 180°, the two congruent angles both measure 90°. In each triangle, the larger acute angle measures 60°, so the smaller acute angle measures 30°.

Suggested Questions Students should also discover that the length of the side opposite the 30° angle is half the length of the hypotenuse. If not, ask:

- *What is the length of segment* CP? (Since it is half the length of segment BC, it has a length of 2.)

- *What is the length of the hypotenuse of right triangle* ACP? (4)

- *What is the relationship between the side opposite the 30° angle and the hypotenuse?* (The side opposite the 30° angle is half the length of the hypotenuse.)

In Question B, for an equilateral triangle with side lengths *s*, all students should be able to find the length of the third side of the right triangle (or the reflection line in this example) using the Pythagorean Theorem. Many students will struggle to see that the length of the longer leg is $\sqrt{3}$ times the length of the shorter leg (see answers for calculations). Depending on time, interest, and your students' sophistication with these ideas, you can help them to see this.

There are two common approaches, which refer back to ideas from the seventh-grade unit *Stretching and Shrinking*.

Approach 1: Ratios Have students compare the decimal approximation for the longer leg to the length of the shorter leg using ratios. In each 30-60-90 triangle, the result will be about 1.732,

which is approximately the square root of 3. The conclusion is that the longer leg is 1.732 times (or the square root of 3 times) the length of the shorter leg.

Approach 2: Scale factor Have students find the scale factor from the original 30-60-90 triangle, whose hypotenuse is 1 unit, to each of the others in this problem. For instance, the scale factor from the original triangle to the 30-60-90 triangle whose hypotenuse is 4. Therefore, the length of the longer leg in the 30-60-90 triangle with hypotenuse of 4 units is $2 \cdot \sqrt{3}$. For a general 30-60-90 right triangle with hypotenuse of *s* units, the legs of the triangle are $\frac{s}{2}$ and $\frac{s}{2} \cdot \sqrt{3}$.

Suggested Questions Ask:

- *Suppose you had started with a larger equilateral triangle. Would your rule have been different? What if you had started with a smaller equilateral triangle?* (If students are still having difficulties, give them another equilateral triangle with side lengths of 5 or 6 units to try.)

- *Would your rule be true of any 30-60-90 triangle?*

You may need to cut out several 30-60-90 triangles to demonstrate that two copies can always be placed back to back to make an equilateral triangle. This is an opportunity to review the properties of similar triangles. Students may need to review that all 60-60-60 triangles are equilateral and are similar. In similar triangles, the ratios of the lengths of corresponding sides are equal. So, in a 30-60-90 triangle, the ratio of the length of the side opposite the 30° angle to the length of the hypotenuse is also 1 to 2, or $\frac{1}{2}$. If necessary, use other lengths for the sides of the equilateral triangle so students can see that the relationship among the sides remains the same.

Question C of the problems reviews the relationship in a 30-60-90 triangle.

Check for Understanding

As a final summary, you might have students look for the same kinds of relationships in the triangles formed by drawing one diagonal in a square.

Mathematics Background

For background on 45-45 and 30-60 right triangles, see pages 7–8.

Analyzing Triangles

Mathematical Goal

- Investigate the special properties of a 30-60-90 triangle

Launch

Show a transparency of the Getting Ready for Problem 4.3. Tell the class that triangle *ABC* is an equilateral triangle and discuss reflection line of symmetry.

- *What is true about the lengths of the sides of an equilateral triangle?*
- *What is true about the sum and measures of the angles of an equilateral triangle?*

Students should discover that line segment *AP* divides triangle *ABC* into two congruent triangles. Remind students of the formal and informal meaning of congruent triangles.

- *What can you say about the measures of angles and segments of the two congruent triangles?*
- *What can you say about triangles ACP and ABP?*

In Problem 4.3, students will continue to explore these relationships about angles and side lengths. Students can work on this problem in pairs.

Materials
- Transparency 4.3A
- Scissors

Vocabulary
- 30-60-90 triangle

Explore

If students are having trouble, ask questions to help them see that two right triangles were formed by the line of symmetry. Then, ask what else they know about these right triangles.

Make sure students are determining the side lengths by using the Pythagorean Theorem, not by measuring.

Materials
- Transparency 4.3B

Summarize

Let several pairs share their reasoning about each question, demonstrating their work at the board or overhead.

Students should also discover that the length of the side opposite the 30° angle is half the length of the hypotenuse. If not, ask:

- *What is the length of segment CP? Segment AC?*

In Question B, all students should be able to find the length of the third side of the right triangle using the Pythagorean Theorem. Use one of the two possible approaches to help clarify student confusion related to Question B.

Question C reviews the relationships in a 30-60-90 triangle.

Materials
- Student notebooks
- Transparency 4.3B

ACE Assignment Guide for Problem 4.3

Core 10, 11
Other *Connections* 26–34; *Extensions* 47–52; unassigned choices from earlier problems

Adapted For suggestions about adapting ACE exercises, see the CMP *Special Needs Handbook*.
Connecting to Prior Units 26: *Filling and Wrapping*; 28: *Stretching and Shrinking*; 29–31: *Bits and Pieces I*

Answers to Problem 4.3

A. Since triangles *ACP* and *APB* are congruent, measures of corresponding angles and sides are equal.

1. Angle *CAP* measures 30°; Angle *CAB* measures 60° because it is an angle of the original equilateral triangle, angle *CAP* has a measure equal to half of angle *CAB* or 30° because *AP* is a line of reflection.

2. Angle *BAP* measures 30° since it is congruent to angle *CAP*.

3. Angle *CPA* measures 90° because each is half of 180°.

4. Angle *BPA* measures 90° because each is half of 180°.

5. Length of *CP* is 2 units. The length of side *CP* is equal to half of a side of the equilateral triangle or half of 4, since *AP* is a line of reflection.

6. Length of *PB* is 2 units.

7. Length of *AP* is $2\sqrt{3}$ units; Because triangle *APB* is a right triangle, and $4^2 - 2^2 = 12$, the length of side *AP* is $\sqrt{12}$ or $2\sqrt{3}$ units.

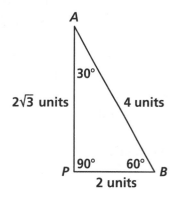

B. The same pattern will hold for any triangle *ABC* with side length *s*: There are two congruent triangles for each case; angle measures of the triangles obtained by a line of reflection are again 30-60-90 degrees.

1. Angle *CAP* measures 30°.

2. Angle *BAP* measures 30°.

3. Angle *CPA* measures 90°.

4. Angle *BPA* measures 90°.

5. Length of *CP* is $\frac{1}{2}s$ units.

6. Length of *PB* is $\frac{1}{2}s$ units.

7. Length of *AP* is $\frac{s}{2}\sqrt{3}$; The ratio of the length of the side opposite the 30° angle to the length of the hypotenuse is always 1 to 2, so the lengths of *PB* and *CP* are $\frac{s}{2}$. The length of *AP* is $\sqrt{s^2 - \frac{s^2}{4}} = \sqrt{\frac{3s^2}{4}} = \frac{s}{2}\sqrt{3}$. Notice that the ratio of the length of the side opposite the 60° to the length of the side opposite the 30° angle is always $\sqrt{3}$. Therefore, in a 30-60-90 triangle the length of the longer leg is $\sqrt{3}$ times the length of the shorter leg. Not all students will notice this. They can, however, always apply the Pythagorean Theorem.

C. 1. The length of the side opposite the 30° angle is half the length of the hypotenuse, or 3 units. Because $6^2 - 3^2 = 27$, the length of the other leg is $\sqrt{27}$ units or $3\sqrt{3}$ units.

2. As explained in Question B, the ratio of the length of the side opposite the 30° angle to the length of the hypotenuse is always 1 to 2, and the ratio of the length of the side opposite the 30° to the length of the side opposite the 60° angle is always 1 to $\sqrt{3}$.

Goal

- Use the properties of special right triangles to solve problems

In this problem, students will apply what they have learned about the Pythagorean Theorem and the special properties of 30-60-90 triangles.

Launch 4.4

Display Transparency 4.4 on the overhead.

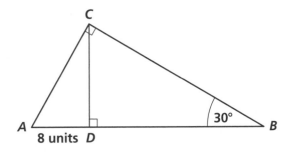

Suggested Questions Ask:

- *Look at triangle ABC. What do you need to know to find its perimeter?* (The lengths of the sides)

- *How can we find those lengths?*

Let students offer their ideas. They may notice that the length of the side opposite the 30° angle in triangle *ABC* must be half the length of the hypotenuse but that neither of those two lengths is given. Some may notice that the measure of angle *CAB* must be 60°, because the sum of the measures of the other two angles in triangle *ABC* is 120°.

- *The challenge for you in this problem is to reason about the relationships in 30-60-90 triangles and the measures that are given to find the side lengths of triangle ABC and calculate the perimeter.*

Have the class work in groups of four on the problem.

Explore 4.4

Circulate as groups explore the problem. Some may need help identifying the three 30-60-90 triangles embedded in the figure. Suggest they draw the three triangles separately as shown here:

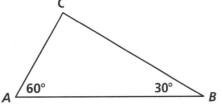

Students may have different strategies for determining the missing measures. Some may start with triangle *BCD*, some with triangle *ABC*.

Suggested Questions Ask:

- *How can you find the measure of angle BCD?* [This is a right triangle, so the measure is 180° − (90° + 30°) = 60°.]

- *How can you find the measure of angle CAD?* (You can use triangle *ABC* or triangle *ACD*. In the latter case, you will need to find the measure of angle *ACD* first.)

Encourage groups to keep track of their calculations in an orderly way so they will be able to explain their reasoning to the class.

Ask one of the groups to describe how they found the perimeter of *ABC*. Here is one possible explanation:

Because the two labeled angles in triangle *ABC* have measures 30° and 90°, the measure of angle *CAB* must be 180° − 120°, or 60°. Therefore, angle *ACD* measures 180° − 150° = 30°, and angle *DCB* measures 90° − 30° = 60°.

The side opposite the 30° angle in right triangle *ACD* has a length of 8 units. The length of the hypotenuse, side *AC*, must be twice that, or 16 units.

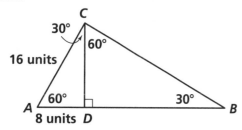

Because side *AB* is the hypotenuse of the 30-60-90 triangle *ABC* and the length of the side opposite the 30° angle is 16 units, the length of the hypotenuse, or side *AB*, must be twice that, or 32 units.

We can now apply the Pythagorean Theorem to find the missing side length of triangle *ABC*. Because one leg and the hypotenuse measure

16 units and 32 units, respectively, the length of side *BC* is the square root of $32^2 - 16^2$, or $\sqrt{768}$.

The perimeter of triangle *ABC* is thus $16 + 32 + \sqrt{768} \approx 16 + 32 + 27.7 \approx 75.7$ units.

Move on to the rest of the questions. Some students may recall the properties of a 30-60-90 triangle and realize that the length of *BC* is $16\sqrt{3}$.

Suggested Questions Once students have discussed how they found the areas of the triangles, ask:

● *What is the relationship between the areas of the two smaller triangles and the area of the largest triangle?* (The sum of the areas of the two smaller triangles is equal to the area of the largest triangle.)

● *Which triangles are similar? Why?*

● *For each pair of similar triangles, what is the ratio of the short leg to the long leg? The short leg to the hypotenuse?*

4.4 Finding the Perimeter

Mathematical Goal

- Use the properties of special right triangles to solve problems

Launch

Display Transparency 4.4 on the overhead.

- *Look at triangle ABC. What do you need to know to find its perimeter? How can we find those lengths?*

Let students offer their ideas.

- *The challenge for you in this problem is to reason about the relationships in 30-60-90 triangles and about the measures that are given to find the side lengths of triangle ABC and then to calculate the perimeter.*

Have the class work in groups of four on the problem.

Materials
- Transparency 4.4
- Labsheet 4.4

Explore

Circulate as groups explore the problem. Some may need help identifying the three 30-60-90 triangles embedded in the figure. Suggest they draw the three triangles separately.

- *How can you find the measure of angle BCD? How can you find the measure of angle CAD?*

Encourage groups to keep track of their calculations in an orderly way so they will be able to explain their reasoning to the class.

Summarize

Ask one of the groups to describe how they found the perimeter of ABC.

Move on to the rest of the questions. Once students have discussed how they found the areas of the triangles, ask:

- *What is the relationship between the areas of the two smaller triangles and the area of the largest triangle?*

Materials
- Student notebooks

ACE Assignment Guide for Problem 4.4

Differentiated Instruction
Solutions for All Learners

Core 12, 35
Other *Extensions* 53–58; unassigned choices from earlier problems

Adapted For suggestions about adapting ACE exercises, see the CMP *Special Needs Handbook*.
Connecting to Prior Units 35: *Stretching and Shrinking*

Answers to Problem 4.4

A. Side AC has a length of 16 units, side AB has a length of 32 units, and side BC has a length of $\sqrt{768}$, or $16\sqrt{3}$ units. The perimeter of triangle ABC is thus $16 + 32 + \sqrt{768} \approx 75.7$ units. Answers will vary. See the possible explanation in the Summarize section.

B. The area of triangle ABC is $\frac{1}{2}bh = \frac{1}{2} \cdot 16 \cdot \sqrt{768} \approx 221.7$ units^2 or equivalently $\frac{1}{2} \cdot 32 \cdot \sqrt{192} \approx 221.7$ units^2.

C. Using the Pythagorean Theorem, because $16^2 - 8^2 = 192$, the length of side CD is $\sqrt{192}$, or $8\sqrt{3}$ units. So, the area of triangle ACD is $\frac{1}{2}bh = \frac{1}{2} \cdot 8 \cdot \sqrt{192} \approx 55.4$ units^2. The length of side BD is $32 - 8 = 24$ units, so the area of triangle BCD is $\frac{1}{2} \cdot 24 \cdot \sqrt{192} \approx 166.3$ units^2.
Alternatively, some students may argue that the areas of the two smaller triangles need to add to the area of the largest triangle. These students will use the area formula to find the area of one of the smaller triangles, and then subtract from the area of the largest triangle. to find area of the other smaller triangle.

The student edition pages for this
investigation begin on the next page.

Notes _____
_____
_____
_____

Using the Pythagorean Theorem

In Investigation 3, you studied the Pythagorean Theorem, which states:

The area of the square on the hypotenuse of a right triangle is equal to the sum of the areas of the squares on the legs.

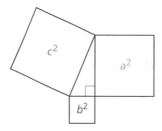

$$a^2 + b^2 = c^2$$

In this investigation, you will explore some interesting applications of the Pythagorean Theorem.

4.1 Analyzing The Wheel of Theodorus

The diagram on the next page is named for its creator, Theodorus of Cyrene (sy ree nee), a former Greek colony. Theodorus was a Pythagorean.

The Wheel of Theodorus begins with a triangle with legs 1 unit long and winds around counterclockwise. Each triangle is drawn using the hypotenuse of the previous triangle as one leg and a segment of length 1 unit as the other leg. To make the Wheel of Theodorus, you need only know how to draw right angles and segments 1 unit long.

STUDENT PAGE

Notes _____

_____

_____

_____

Wheel of Theodorus

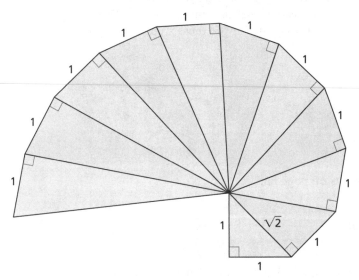

A. Use the Pythagorean Theorem to find the length of each hypotenuse in the Wheel of Theodorus. On a copy of the wheel, label each hypotenuse with its length. Use the $\sqrt{}$ symbol to express lengths that are not whole numbers.

B. Use a cut-out copy of the ruler below to measure each hypotenuse on the wheel. Label the place on the ruler that represents the length of each hypotenuse. For example, the first hypotenuse length would be marked like this:

C. For each hypotenuse length that is not a whole number:

  1. Give the two consecutive whole numbers the length is between. For example, $\sqrt{2}$ is between 1 and 2.

  2. Use your ruler to find two decimal numbers (to the tenths place) the length is between. For example $\sqrt{2}$ is between 1.4 and 1.5.

  3. Use your calculator to estimate the value of each length and compare the result to the approximations you found in part (2).

Investigation 4 Using the Pythagorean Theorem **47**

Notes _____

_____

_____

_____

D. Odakota uses his calculator to find $\sqrt{3}$. He gets 1.732050808. Geeta says this must be wrong because when she multiplies 1.732050808 by 1.732050808, she gets 3.000000001. Why do these students disagree?

ACE Homework starts on page 53.

Did You Know?

Some decimals, such as 0.5 and 0.3125, *terminate*. They have a limited number of digits. Other decimals, such as 0.3333 . . . and 0.181818 . . . , have a repeating pattern of digits that never ends.

Terminating or repeating decimals are called **rational numbers** because they can be expressed as *ratios* of integers.

$$0.5 = \frac{1}{2} \qquad 0.3125 = \frac{5}{16} \qquad 0.3333 \ldots = \frac{1}{3} \qquad 0.181818 \ldots = \frac{2}{11}.$$

Some decimals neither terminate nor repeat. The decimal representation of the number π starts with the digits 3.14159265 . . . and goes forever without any repeating sequence of digits. Numbers with non-terminating and non-repeating decimal representations are called **irrational numbers.** They cannot be expressed as ratios of integers.

The number $\sqrt{2}$ is an irrational number. You had trouble finding an exact terminating or repeating decimal representation for $\sqrt{2}$ because such a representation does not exist. Other irrational numbers are $\sqrt{3}$, $\sqrt{5}$, and $\sqrt{11}$. In fact, $\sqrt{n}$ is an irrational number for any value of n that is not a square number.

The set of irrational and rational numbers is called the set of **real numbers.** An amazing fact about irrational numbers is that there is an infinite number of them between any two fractions!

STUDENT PAGE

Notes _____

_____

_____

_____

4.2 Stopping Sneaky Sally

You can use the Pythagorean Theorem to solve problems in which you need to find the length of a side of a right triangle.

Problem 4.2 Finding Unknown Side Lengths

Horace Hanson is the catcher for the Humboldt Bees baseball team. Sneaky Sally Smith, the star of the Canfield Cats, is on first base. Sally is known for stealing bases, so Horace is keeping an eye on her.

The pitcher throws a fastball, and the batter swings and misses. Horace catches the pitch and, out of the corner of his eye, he sees Sally take off for second base.

Use the diagram to answer Questions A and B.

A. How far must Horace throw the baseball to get Sally out at second base? Explain.

B. The shortstop is standing on the baseline, halfway between second base and third base. How far is the shortstop from Horace?

C. The pitcher's mound is 60 feet 6 inches from home plate. Use this information and your answer to Question A to find the distance from the pitcher's mound to each base.

ACE Homework starts on page 53.

STUDENT PAGE

Investigation 4 Using the Pythagorean Theorem **49**

Notes _____

_____

_____

_____

Although most people consider baseball an American invention, a similar game, called *rounders*, was played in England as early as the 1600s. Like baseball, rounders involved hitting a ball and running around bases. However, in rounders, the fielders actually threw the ball at the base runners. If a ball hit a runner while he was off base, he was out.

Alexander Cartwright was a founding member of the Knickerbockers Base Ball Club of New York City, baseball's first organized club. Cartwright played a key role in writing the first set of formal rules for baseball in 1845.

According to Cartwright's rules, a batter was out if a fielder caught the ball either on the fly or on the first bounce. Today, balls caught on the first bounce are not outs. Cartwright's rules also stated that the first team to have 21 runs at the end of an inning was the winner. Today, the team with the highest score after nine innings wins the game.

Go **Online**
PHSchool.com

For: Information about Alexander Cartwright
Web Code: ape-9031

4.3 Analyzing Triangles

All equilateral triangles have reflection symmetries. This property and the Pythagorean Theorem can be used to investigate some interesting properties of other equilateral triangles.

Getting Ready for Problem 4.3

Triangle ABC is an equilateral triangle.

- What is true about the angle measures in an equilateral triangle?

- What is true about the side lengths of an equilateral triangle?

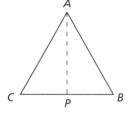

Notes _____

_____

_____

_____

Line *AP* is a reflection line for triangle *ABC*.

- What can you say about the measures of the following angles? Explain.

  Angle *CAP*   Angle *BAP*

  Angle *CPA*   Angle *BPA*

- What can you say about line segments *CP* and *PB*? Explain.

- What can you say about triangles *ACP* and *ABP*?

Problem 4.3 Analyzing Triangles

A. Copy triangle *ABC* on the facing page. If the lengths of the sides of this equilateral triangle are 4 units, label the following measures:

1. angle *CAP*   **2.** angle *BAP*

3. angle *CPA*   **4.** angle *BPA*

5. length of *CP*   **6.** length of *PB*

7. length of *AP*

B. Suppose the lengths of the sides of *ABC* triangles are *s* units. Find the measures of the following:

1. angle *CAP*   **2.** angle *BAP*

3. angle *CPA*   **4.** angle *BPA*

5. length of *CP*   **6.** length of *PB*

7. length of *AP*

C. A right triangle with a 60° angle is called a 30-60-90 triangle. This 30-60-90 triangle has a hypotenuse of length 6 units.

1. What are the lengths of the other two sides? Explain how you found your answers.

2. What relationships among the side lengths do you observe for this 30-60-90 triangle? Is this relationship true for all 30-60-90 triangles? Explain.

ACE Homework starts on page 53.

Notes _____

_____

_____

_____

4.4 Finding the Perimeter

In this problem, you will apply many of the strategies you have developed in this unit, especially what you found in Problem 4.3.

Problem 4.4 Finding the Perimeter

Use the diagram for Questions A–C. Explain your work.

A. Find the perimeter of triangle *ABC*.

B. Find the area of triangle *ABC*.

C. Find the areas of triangle *ACD* and triangle *BCD*.

ACE Homework starts on page 53.

Did You Know?

In the movie *The Wizard of Oz,* the scarecrow celebrates his new brain by reciting the following:

"The sum of the square roots of any two sides of an isosceles triangle is equal to the square root of the remaining side."

Now you know what the scarecrow meant to say, even though his still imperfect brain got it wrong!

Notes

Applications

1. The hypotenuse of a right triangle is 15 centimeters long. One leg is 9 centimeters long. How long is the other leg?

2. The Wheel of Theodorus in Problem 4.1 includes only the first 11 triangles in the wheel. The wheel can go on forever.

   a. Find the side lengths of the next three triangles.

   b. Find the areas of the first five triangles in the wheel. Do you observe any pattern?

   c. Suppose you continue adding triangles to the wheel. Which triangle will have a hypotenuse of length 5 units?

In Exercises 3 and 4, find the missing length.

3.

30 in.

10 in.

d

4.

4 ft

j

12 ft

5. Moesha, a college student, needs to walk from her dorm room in Wilson Hall to her math class in Wells Hall. Normally, she walks 500 meters east and 600 meters north along the sidewalks, but today she is running late. She decides to take the shortcut through the Tundra.

   a. How many meters long is Moesha's shortcut?

   b. How much shorter is the shortcut than Moesha's usual route?

Wells Hall

Shaw Lane

Wilson Hall

The Tundra

600 m

500 m

Investigation 4 Using the Pythagorean Theorem **53**

Notes _____

_____

_____

_____

6. Square *ABCD* has sides of length 1 unit. The diagonal *BD* is a line of reflection.

   a. How do the triangles *ABD* and *BDC* compare?

   b. Find the angle measures for one of the triangles. Explain how you found each measure.

   c. What is the length of the diagonal? Explain.

   d. Suppose square *ABCD* had sides of length 5 units instead of 1 unit. How would this change your answers to parts (b) and (c)?

7. A right triangle with a 45° angle is called a 45-45-90 triangle.

   a. Are all 45-45-90 triangles similar to each other? Explain.

   b. Suppose one leg of a 45-45-90 triangle is 5 units long. Find the perimeter of the triangle.

8. The diagram shows an amusement park ride in which tram cars glide along a cable. How long, to the nearest tenth of a meter, is the cable for the ride?

Not drawn to scale

Notes _____

_____

_____

_____

9. At Emmit's Evergreen Farm, the taller trees are braced by wires.
   A wire extends from 2 feet below the top of a tree to a stake in the
   ground. What is the tallest tree that can be braced with a 25-foot
   wire staked 15 feet from the base of the tree?

10. As part of his math assignment, Denzel has to estimate the height of
    a tower. He decides to use what he knows about 30-60-90 triangles.

    Denzel makes the measurements shown below. About how tall
    is the tower? Explain.

Not drawn to scale

Notes _____
_____
_____
_____

11. a. Name all the 30-60-90 triangles in the figure below. Are all of these triangles similar to each other? Explain.

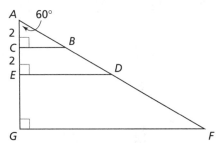

b. Find the ratio of the length of segment *BA* to the length of segment *AC*. What can you say about the corresponding ratio in the other 30-60-90 triangles?

c. Find the ratio of the length of segment *BC* to the length of segment *AC*. What can you say about the corresponding ratios in the other 30-60-90 triangles?

d. Find the ratio of the length of segment *BC* to the length of segment *AB*. What can you say about the corresponding ratios in the other 30-60-90 triangles?

e. Suppose the shortest side of a 30-60-90 triangle is 12 units long. Find the lengths of its other sides.

12. Find the perimeter of triangle *KLM*.

Homework
Help ⬤nline
━━━ PHSchool.com
For: Help with Exercise 12
Web Code: ape-2412

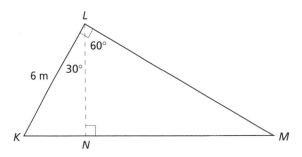

STUDENT PAGE

Notes _____

_____

_____

_____

Connections

Go Online
PHSchool.com

For: Multiple-Choice Skills
Practice
Web Code: apa-2454

Estimate the square root to one decimal place *without* using the
$\sqrt{}$ key on your calculator. Then, tell whether the number is
rational or irrational.

13. $\sqrt{121}$ **14.** $\sqrt{0.49}$ **15.** $\sqrt{15}$ **16.** $\sqrt{1,000}$

**Two cars leave the city of Walleroo at noon. One car travels north and
the other travels east. Use this information for Exercises 17 and 18.**

17. Suppose the northbound car is traveling at 60 miles per hour and
the eastbound car is traveling at 50 miles per hour. Make a table
that shows the distance each car has traveled and the distance
between the two cars after 1 hour, 2 hours, 3 hours, and so on.
Describe how the distances are changing.

18. Suppose the northbound car is traveling at 40 miles per hour. After
2 hours, the cars are 100 miles apart. How fast is the other car going?
Explain.

**Write each fraction as a decimal and tell whether the decimal is terminating
or repeating. If the decimal is repeating, tell which digits repeat.**

19. $\frac{2}{5}$ **20.** $\frac{3}{8}$ **21.** $\frac{5}{6}$ **22.** $\frac{35}{10}$ **23.** $\frac{8}{99}$

**Tell whether a triangle with the given side lengths is a right triangle.
Explain how you know.**

24. 5 cm, 7 cm, $\sqrt{74}$ cm   **25.** $\sqrt{2}$ ft, $\sqrt{7}$ ft, 3 ft

Notes _____

_____

_____

_____

26. The figure at the right is a net for a pyramid.

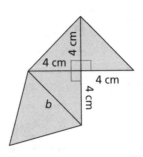

   a. What is the length of side b?

   b. Sketch the pyramid.

   c. What is the surface area of the pyramid?

27. **Multiple Choice** Which set of irrational numbers is in order from least to greatest?

   A. $\sqrt{2}, \sqrt{5}, \sqrt{11}, \pi$

   B. $\sqrt{2}, \sqrt{5}, \pi, \sqrt{11}$

   C. $\sqrt{2}, \pi, \sqrt{5}, \sqrt{11}$

   D. $\pi, \sqrt{2}, \sqrt{5}, \sqrt{11}$

28. In Problem 4.3, you found the side lengths of the triangle on the left.

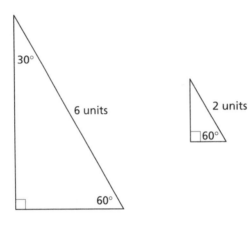

   a. Explain how you know the triangle on the right is similar to the triangle on the left.

   b. Use the side lengths of the larger triangle to find the side lengths of the smaller triangle. Explain.

   c. How are the areas of the triangles related?

Find a fraction equivalent to the terminating decimal.

29. 0.35

30. 2.1456

31. 89.050

For Exercises 32–34, tell whether the statement is *true* or *false*.

32. $0.06 = \sqrt{0.36}$

33. $1.1 = \sqrt{1.21}$

34. $20 = \sqrt{40}$

Notes _____

_____

_____

_____

35. In Problem 4.4, you worked with this triangle.

a. Find the perimeter of triangle ACD.

b. How is the perimeter of triangle ACD related to the perimeter of triangle ABC?

c. How is the area of triangle ACD related to the area of triangle ABC?

Find the two consecutive whole numbers the square root is between. Explain.

36. $\sqrt{39}$ **37.** $\sqrt{600}$

Extensions

38. a. Copy the table at the right. Write each fraction as a decimal.

b. Describe a pattern you see in your table.

c. Use the pattern to write decimal representations for $\frac{9}{9}$, $\frac{10}{9}$, and $\frac{15}{9}$. Use your calculator to check your answers.

d. Find fractions equivalent to $1.\overline{2}$ and $2.\overline{7}$, where the bar means the number under the bar repeats forever. (**Hint:** $1.\overline{2}$ can be written as $1 + 0.22222...$ The bar on the 2 means the 2 repeats forever.)

Fraction	Decimal
$\frac{1}{9}$	
$\frac{2}{9}$	
$\frac{3}{9}$	
$\frac{4}{9}$	
$\frac{5}{9}$	
$\frac{6}{9}$	
$\frac{7}{9}$	
$\frac{8}{9}$	

Investigation 4 Using the Pythagorean Theorem   **59**

Notes _____

_____

_____

_____

39. Explore decimal representations of fractions with a denominator of 99. Look at fractions less than one, $\frac{1}{99}$, $\frac{2}{99}$, $\frac{3}{99}$, and so on. What patterns do you see?

40. Explore decimal representations of fractions with a denominator of 999. Look at fractions less than one, $\frac{1}{999}$, $\frac{2}{999}$, $\frac{3}{999}$, and so on. What patterns do you see?

Use the patterns you discovered in Exercises 38–40 to find a fraction or mixed number equivalent to each decimal.

41. 0.3333 . . .   **42.** 0.050505 . . .   **43.** 0.454545 . . .

44. 0.045045 . . .   **45.** 10.121212 . . .   **46.** 3.9999 . . .

For Exercises 47 and 48, find the length of the diagonal d.

47.

12 cm

d

3 cm

4 cm

48.

d

$\sqrt{111}$ cm

6 cm

7 cm

49. Segment AB below makes a 45° angle with the x-axis. The length of segment AB is 5 units.

a. Find the coordinates of point B to two decimal places.

b. What is the slope of line AB?

60   Looking for Pythagoras

Notes _____

_____

_____

_____

In Exercises 50–52, you will look for relationships among the areas of similar shapes other than squares drawn on the sides of a right triangle.

50. Half-circles have been drawn on the sides of this right triangle.

    a. Find the area of each half-circle.

    b. How are the areas of the half-circles related?

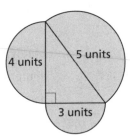

51. Equilateral triangles have been drawn on the sides of this right triangle.

    a. Find the area of each equilateral triangle.

    b. How are the areas of the equilateral triangles related?

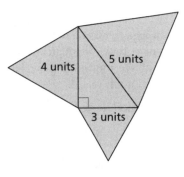

Extensions

52. Regular hexagons have been drawn on the sides of this right triangle.

    a. Find the area of each hexagon.

    b. How are the areas of the hexagons related?

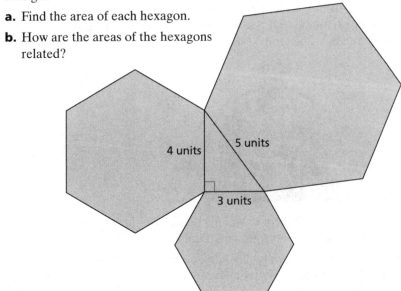

53. Find an irrational number between 6.23 and 6.35.

Investigation 4 Using the Pythagorean Theorem   **61**

STUDENT PAGE

Notes _____

_____

_____

_____

54. You can use algebra to help you write a repeating decimal as a fraction. For example, suppose you want to write 0.12121212 ... as a fraction.

Let $x = 0.12121212 \ldots$

$100x = 12.12121212 \ldots$ Multiply both sides by 100.

$\underline{-\ \ x = 0.12121212 \ldots}$ Subtract the first equation from the second.

$99x = 12$

Divide both sides of the resulting equation, $99x = 12$, by 99 to get $x = \frac{12}{99}$. So, $0.12121212 \ldots = \frac{12}{99}$.

The key to this method is to multiply each side of the original equation by a power of 10 (such, as 10, 100, or 1,000) that shifts one group of repeating digits to the left of the decimal point. In the example above, multiplying by 100 shifted one "12" to the left of the decimal point.

Use the method described above to write each decimal as a fraction.

a. 0. 15151515 ...   **b.** 0. 7777 ...   **c.**   0.123123123123 ...

55. When building a barn, a farmer must make sure the sides are perpendicular to the ground.

a. One method for checking whether a wall is perpendicular to the ground involves using a 10-foot pole. The farmer makes a mark exactly 6 feet high on the wall. She then places one end of the pole on the mark and the other end on the ground.

How far from the base of the wall will the pole touch the ground if the wall is perpendicular to the ground? Explain.

b. You may have heard the saying, "I wouldn't touch that with a 10-foot pole!" What would this saying mean to a farmer who had just built a barn?

c. Suppose a farmer uses a 15-foot pole and makes a mark 12 feet high on the wall. How far from the base of the wall will the pole touch the ground if the wall is perpendicular to the ground?

62   Looking for Pythagoras

Notes _____

_____

_____

_____

d. Name another pole length a farmer could use. For this length how high should the mark on the wall be? How far from the base of the wall will the pole touch the ground?

56. Find the perimeter of triangle *ABC*.

57. Below is the net for a square pyramid and a sketch of the pyramid.

a. What is the area of the base of the pyramid?

b. What is the surface area of the pyramid?

c. What is the height of the pyramid?

d. What is the volume of the pyramid?

58. The managers of Izzie's Ice Cream Shop are trying to decide on the best size for their cones.

a. Izzie thinks the cone should have a diameter of 4.5 inches and a height of 6 inches. What is the volume of the cone Izzie suggests?

b. Izzie's sister Becky thinks the cone should have a height of 6 inches and a slant height of 7 inches. (The slant height is labeled *s* in the diagram at the right.) What is the volume of the cone Becky suggests?

Notes _____

_____

_____

_____

Mathematical Reflections 4

In this investigation, you applied the ideas from the first three investigations. The following questions will help you summarize what you have learned.

Think about your answers to these questions. Discuss your ideas with other students and your teacher. Then write a summary of your findings in your notebook.

1. In what ways is the Pythagorean Theorem useful? Give at least two examples.

2. Describe the special properties of a 30-60-90 triangle.

Notes _____

_____

_____

_____

Investigation

ACE
Assignment Choices

Differentiated Instruction
Solutions for All Learners

Problem 4.1
Core 1, 2
Other *Connections* 13–16

Problem 4.2
Core 3–5, 24, 25
Other *Applications* 6–9; *Connections* 17–23, 36, 37; *Extensions* 38–46; unassigned choices from earlier problems

Problem 4.3
Core 10, 11
Other *Connections* 26–34; *Extensions* 47–52; unassigned choices from earlier problems

Problem 4.4
Core 12, 35
Other *Extensions* 53–58; unassigned choices from earlier problems

Adapted For suggestions about adapting Exercise 8 and other ACE exercises, see the CMP *Special Needs Handbook*.
Connecting to Prior Units 17–18: *Moving Straight Ahead*; 26: *Filling and Wrapping*; 28, 35: *Stretching and Shrinking*; 29–31: *Bits and Pieces I*

Applications

1. 12 cm

2. **a.** The 12th triangle has leg lengths 1 unit and $\sqrt{12}$ units and hypotenuse length $\sqrt{13}$ units. The 13th triangle has leg lengths 1 unit and $\sqrt{13}$ units and hypotenuse length $\sqrt{14}$ units. The 14th triangle has leg lengths 1 unit and $\sqrt{14}$ units and hypotenuse length $\sqrt{15}$ units.
   b. $\frac{1}{2}$ sq. unit, $\frac{1}{2} \cdot \sqrt{2}$ units^2, $\frac{1}{2} \cdot \sqrt{3}$ units^2, $\frac{1}{2} \cdot \sqrt{4}$ units^2, 1 unit^2, $\frac{1}{2} \cdot \sqrt{5}$ units^2.

The number under the square root sign increases by 1 for every new triangle. Or, the area of the nth triangle is $\frac{1}{2} \cdot \sqrt{n}$.
   c. 5 is the square root of 25. So, the hypotenuse length of the 24th triangle is 5 units.

3. $\sqrt{900 - 100} = \sqrt{800} \approx 28.28$ in.

4. $\sqrt{144 - 16} = \sqrt{128} \approx 11.31$ ft

5. **a.** Because $500^2 + 600^2 = 610,000$, the distance is $\sqrt{610,000} \approx 781$ m.
   b. $1,100 - 781 \approx 319$ m

6. **a.** They are congruent.
   b. 45°, 45°, 90°. The diagonal divides the corner angles into two equal angles, so the smaller angles must each be half of 90°, or 45°. Some students may use a protractor or angle ruler.
   c. The legs of the right triangle each have a length of 1 unit, and $1^2 + 1^2 = 2$. So the diagonal—which is the hypotenuse of a right triangle—has a length of $\sqrt{2}$ units.
   d. The measures of the angles would still be 45°, 45°, and 90°. Because $5^2 + 5^2 = 50$, the length of the diagonal would be $\sqrt{50}$ units. (**Note:** Some students may notice that $\sqrt{50} = \sqrt{25 \cdot 2} = 5\sqrt{2}$, or that this square is larger than the original by a scale factor of 5; thus, the diagonal must be 5 times as long, or $5\sqrt{2}$ units.)

7. **a.** All 45-45-90 triangles are similar to each other. If corresponding angles of a triangle are congruent, then the triangles are similar.
   b. The other leg must also be 5 units long because 45-45-90 triangles are isosceles. Applying the Pythagorean Theorem we have $(\text{hypotenuse})^2 = 5^2 + 5^2 = 50$, so hypotenuse $= \sqrt{50} = 5\sqrt{2} \approx 7.07$ units. So, the perimeter is $5 + 5 + 5\sqrt{2} \approx 17.07$ units.

ACE ANSWERS 4

8. 1012.4 m. The first segment along the ground is the leg of an isosceles right triangle. Because the other leg is 15 m long, this leg also has a length of 15 m. The same argument holds for the last segment along the ground. Therefore, the horizontal portion of cable is $1{,}000 - (2 \cdot 15) = 970$ m long. Each angled part of the cable is the hypotenuse of an isosceles right triangle with legs of length 15 units. Because $15^2 + 15^2 = 450$, each angled piece has length $\sqrt{450} \approx 21.2$ m. The overall length of the cable is thus $970 + 21.2 + 21.2 \approx 1012.4$ m.

9. 22 ft. Because $25^2 - 15^2 = 400$, the tallest tree that can be braced is $\sqrt{400}$ ft, or 20 ft tall at the point of attachment. Adding 2 ft gives a total height of 22 ft. (**Note:** You can point out to students that this is a 3-4-5 Pythagorean Triple with a scale factor of 5.)

10. About 105.5 ft. The leg along the bottom of the 30-60-90 triangle measures 58 ft. The hypotenuse (from Denzel's eyes to the top of the tower) is twice as long, or 116 ft. Because $116^2 - 58^2 = 10{,}092$, the vertical leg measures $\sqrt{10{,}092} \approx 100.5$ ft. Adding the distance from the ground to Denzel's eyes, the tower is about 105.5 ft tall.

11. **a.** *ABC, ADE,* and *AFG* are 30-60-90 triangles. The measure of angle *A*, which is in all three triangles, is 60°. Angles *ACB*, *AED*, and *AGF* all have measure 90° because the segments that form their sides are perpendicular (one side is horizontal and the other is vertical). So, the third angles of the three triangles—*ABC, ADE,* and *AFG*—must all have measure 30°. These triangles are all similar because if corresponding angles of a triangle are congruent, then the triangles are similar.

   b. $\frac{BA}{AC} = \frac{4}{2} = \frac{2}{1}$. The length of *AC* is 2 units and, because triangle *ABC* is a 30-60-90 triangle, *BA* is twice the length of the side opposite the 30° angle, which is *AC*. Therefore, the length of *BA* is 4 units. The corresponding ratio for the other two triangles must be the same because the triangles are similar.

   c. $\frac{BC}{AC} = \frac{2\sqrt{3}}{2} = \sqrt{3}$. Possible explanation: In a 30-60-90 triangle, the length of the side

opposite the 60° angle is $\sqrt{3}$ times the length of the side opposite the 30° angle, which is *AC*. *AC* has length 2 units, so *BC* has length $2\sqrt{3}$ units. So, $\frac{BC}{AC} = \frac{2\sqrt{3}}{2} = \sqrt{3}$. The corresponding ratio for the other two triangles must be the same because the triangles are similar.

   d. $\frac{BC}{AB} = \frac{2\sqrt{3}}{4} = \frac{\sqrt{3}}{2}$. The corresponding ratio for the other two triangles must be the same because the triangles are similar.

   e. 24 units and $12\sqrt{3}$ units. Possible explanation: Triangle *XYZ* fits the description given in the problem.

The ratio $\frac{YZ}{XZ}$ must be equal to $\sqrt{3}$ because *XYZ* is similar to triangle *ABC* in part (a). Therefore, $YZ = XZ \cdot \sqrt{3} = 12\sqrt{3}$. In all 30-60-90 triangles, the ratio of the hypotenuse to the shortest side is 2:1. So $XY = 2 \cdot 12 = 24$.

12. About 28.39 m. All triangles in the diagram are 30-60-90 triangles. The hypotenuse of the large triangle is 12 m (twice the shorter leg that is given). The longer leg is $6\sqrt{3}$, or $\sqrt{108} \approx 10.39$. This last leg can be found with the Pythagorean Theorem or by applying a scale factor of 6 to the 30-60-90 triangle in Question A of Problem 4.3.

Connections

13. $\sqrt{121} = 11$; rational

14. $\sqrt{0.49} = 0.7$; rational

15. $\sqrt{15} \approx 3.9$; irrational

16. $\sqrt{1000} \approx 31.6$; irrational

17. See Figure 2. The distance between the cars increases by 78.1 mi each hour. (**Note:** Students will probably calculate the distance apart by adding the sum of the squares and taking the square root of that sum.)

18. After 2 hr, the northbound car has traveled 80 mi. Use this distance as one leg of a right triangle and the distance apart (100 mi) as the hypotenuse. Using the Pythagorean Theorem, $100^2 - 80^2 = 3{,}600$, so the distance the eastbound car has traveled must be $\sqrt{3{,}600} = 60$ mi. This distance was traveled in 2 hr, so the eastbound car is traveling at 30 mph. (**Note:** This is a 3-4-5 right triangle with a scale factor of 20.)

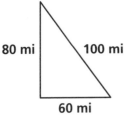

19. $\frac{2}{5} = 0.4$; terminating

20. $\frac{3}{8} = 0.375$; terminating

21. $\frac{5}{6} = 0.8333\ldots$; 3 repeats

22. $\frac{35}{10} = 3.5$; terminating

23. $\frac{8}{99} = 0.08080808\ldots$; 08 repeats

24. Right triangle. $5^2 + 7^2 = (\sqrt{74})^2$

25. Right triangle.
$(\sqrt{2})^2 + (\sqrt{7})^2 = 2 + 7 = 9 = 3^2$

26. a. $\sqrt{32} \approx 5.66$ cm

b.

c. About 37.9

27. B

28. a. Two pairs of corresponding angles are equal, so the triangles are similar.

b. Because the triangles are similar, the corresponding sides are proportional. The given side length of the smaller triangle is a third of the corresponding side length of the larger triangle, so the other two side lengths of the smaller triangle must also be a third the length of the corresponding sides of the larger triangle. The sides of the larger triangle are 6 units, 3 units, and $3\sqrt{3}$ or $\sqrt{27}$ units (or about 5.2 units), so the sides of the smaller triangle are 2 units, 1 unit, and $\sqrt{3}$ or $\frac{1}{3}\sqrt{27}$ units (or about 1.7 units).

c. The larger triangle's area is 9 times the smaller triangle's area.

29. Possible answers: $\frac{35}{100}$ or $\frac{7}{20}$

Figure 2

Hours	Distance Traveled by Northbound Car (mi)	Distance Traveled by Eastbound Car (mi)	Distance Between Cars (mi)
1	60	50	$\sqrt{60^2 + 50^2} \approx 78.1$
2	120	100	$\sqrt{120^2 + 100^2} \approx 156.2$
3	180	150	$\sqrt{180^2 + 150^2} \approx 234.3$
4	240	200	$\sqrt{240^2 + 200^2} \approx 312.4$
n	$60n$	$50n$	$78.1n$

30. Possible answer: $\frac{21,456}{10,000}$

31. Possible answer: $\frac{89,050}{1,000}$

32. False. $0.06 \cdot 0.06 = 0.0036$

33. True. $1.1 \cdot 1.1 = 1.21$

34. False. $20 \cdot 20 = 400$

35. a. About 37.9 units. $AC = 16$ units, $CD = \sqrt{192}$ units, or $8\sqrt{3}$ units, or about 13.9 units. So the perimeter is about $16 + 8 + 13.9$, or 37.9 units.

b. Because triangle BDC is a 30-60-90 triangle, we can use the length of AC to get the length of AB, which is 32 units, and of BC, which is $16\sqrt{3}$ units. So the perimeter of triangle ABC is $32 + 16 + 16\sqrt{3}$, or about 75.7 units. We could have arrived at this answer without any calculation by noticing that the triangles are similar and the scale factor is 2. Therefore, the perimeter of triangle ABC is twice the perimeter of triangle ACD.

c. The area of triangle ABC is 4 times the area of triangle ACD.

36. 6 and 7. $6^2 = 36$ and $7^2 = 49$. Because 39 is between 36 and 49, $\sqrt{39}$ is between 6 and 7.

37. 24 and 25. $24^2 = 576$ and $25^2 = 625$. Because 600 is between 576 and 625, $\sqrt{600}$ is between 24 and 25.

Extensions

38. a.

Fraction	Decimal
$\frac{1}{9}$	0.1111...
$\frac{2}{9}$	0.2222...
$\frac{3}{9}$	0.3333...
$\frac{4}{9}$	0.4444...
$\frac{5}{9}$	0.5555...
$\frac{6}{9}$	0.6666...
$\frac{7}{9}$	0.7777...
$\frac{8}{9}$	0.8888...

b. Each fraction is equivalent to a repeating decimal. The repeating part is a single digit that is equal to the numerator of the fraction.

c. 0.9999 ... or 1; 1.111 ...; 1.666 ...

d. $1.2222 \ldots = 1 + 0.222 \ldots = 1 + \frac{2}{9} = 1\frac{2}{9}$
$2.7777 \ldots = 2 + 0.777 \ldots = 2 + \frac{7}{9} = 2\frac{7}{9}$

39. $\frac{1}{99} = 0.010101 \ldots, \frac{2}{99} = 0.020202 \ldots,$ $\frac{3}{99} = 0.030303 \ldots$ A fraction with a denominator of 99 is equal to a repeating decimal. For numerators less than 99, the repeating part has two digits: either a 0 followed by the number in the numerator if that number is less than 10 or the number in the numerator if that number is greater than 10.

40. $\frac{1}{999} = 0.001001001 \ldots,$ $\frac{2}{999} = 0.002002002 \ldots,$ $\frac{3}{999} = 0.003003003 \ldots$ A fraction with a denominator of 999 is equal to a repeating decimal. For numerators less than 999, the repeating part has three digits: two 0s followed by the number in the numerator if that number is less than 10; one 0 followed by the number in the numerator if that number is greater than 10 and less than 100; or the number in the numerator if that number is greater than 100.

41. $\frac{1}{3}$ **42.** $\frac{5}{99}$ **43.** $\frac{45}{99}$

44. $\frac{45}{999}$ **45.** $10\frac{12}{99}$ **46.** $3\frac{9}{9}$ or 4

47. The bottom of the box has sides of length 3 cm and 4 cm. Because $3^2 + 4^2 = 25$, the diagonal of the bottom has length $\sqrt{25}$ cm, or 5 cm. Using this as a leg of a right triangle with hypotenuse d, $d^2 = 5^2 + 12^2 = 169$, so $d = \sqrt{169}$ cm $= 13$ cm.

48. The bottom has sides of length 6 cm and 7 cm. Because $6^2 + 7^2 = 85$, the diagonal of the bottom has length $\sqrt{85}$ cm. Using this as a leg of the right triangle with hypotenuse d, $d^2 = (\sqrt{85})^2 + (\sqrt{111})^2 = 85 + 111 = 196$, so $d = \sqrt{196}$ cm $= 14$ cm.

49. a. (3.54, 3.54). Draw a vertical segment from B down to the x-axis to create a 45-45-90 triangle ABC.

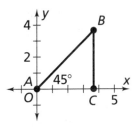

As observed in Exercise 7, in 45-45-90 triangles, the length of the hypotenuse is $\sqrt{2}$ times the length of the leg. So $BC = AC = \frac{5}{\sqrt{2}}$ units, which is approximately 3.54 units. So, the coordinates of B are (3.54, 3.54).

b. 1

50. a. The half-circle on the leg of length 3 units has area $\frac{1}{2} \cdot \pi \cdot 1.5^2 \approx 3.5$ units^2. The half-circle on the leg of length 4 units has area $\frac{1}{2} \cdot \pi \cdot 2^2 \approx 6.3$ units^2. The half-circle on the hypotenuse has area $\frac{1}{2} \cdot \pi \cdot 2.5^2 \approx 9.8$ units^2.

b. The sum of the areas of the half-circles on the legs is equal to the area of the half-circle on the hypotenuse: $3.5 + 6.3 = 9.8$.

51. a. Each equilateral triangle can be divided into two 30-60-90 triangles. The equilateral triangle on the leg of length 3 units is composed of two right triangles, each with a leg of length 1.5 units and a hypotenuse of length 3 units. Because $3^2 - 1.5^2 = 6.75$, the longer leg (which is the height of the equilateral triangle) has length $\sqrt{6.75} \approx 2.6$ units. This equilateral triangle has an area of about $\frac{1}{2} \cdot 3 \cdot 2.6 = 3.9$ sq. units. The equilateral triangle on the leg of length 4 units is composed of two right triangles, each with a leg of length 2 units and a hypotenuse of length 4 units. Because $4^2 - 2^2 = 12$, the longer leg has length $\sqrt{12} \approx 3.46$ units. This equilateral triangle

has an area of about $\frac{1}{2} \cdot 4 \cdot 3.46 = 6.9$ units^2. The equilateral triangle on the hypotenuse is composed of two right triangles, each with a leg of length 2.5 units and a hypotenuse of length 5 units. Because $5^2 - 2.5^2 = 18.75$, the longer leg has length $\sqrt{18.75} \approx 4.3$ units. This equilateral triangle has an area of about $\frac{1}{2} \cdot 5 \cdot 4.3 = 10.8$ units^2.

b. The sum of the areas of the equilateral triangles on the legs is equal to the area of the equilateral triangle on the hypotenuse: $3.9 + 6.9 = 10.8$.

52. a. Each hexagon can be divided into six equilateral triangles, the areas of which were found in ACE Exercise 51. The hexagon on the leg of length 3 units has an area of about $6 \cdot 3.9 = 23.4$ units^2. The hexagon on the leg of length 4 has an area of about $6 \cdot 6.9 = 41.4$ units^2. The hexagon on the hypotenuse has an area of about $6 \cdot 10.8 = 64.8$ units^2.

b. The sum of the areas of the hexagons on the legs is equal to the area of the hexagon on the hypotenuse: $23.4 + 41.4 = 64.8$.

53. Possible answers: $\sqrt{39}$, $\sqrt{40}$, and 2π.

54. a. $\begin{aligned} 100x &= 15.15151515\ldots \\ -x &= 0.15151515\ldots \\ \hline 99x &= 15 \\ x &= \tfrac{15}{99} \text{ or } \tfrac{5}{33} \end{aligned}$

b. $\begin{aligned} 10x &= 7.7777\ldots \\ -x &= 0.7777\ldots \\ \hline 9x &= 7 \\ x &= \tfrac{7}{9} \end{aligned}$

c. $\begin{aligned} 1{,}000x &= 123.123123123123\ldots \\ -x &= 0.123123123123\ldots \\ \hline 999x &= 123 \\ x &= \tfrac{123}{999} \text{ or } \tfrac{41}{333} \end{aligned}$

55. a. $\sqrt{100 - 36} = \sqrt{64} = 8$ ft

b. The farmer is saying that the barn is not perpendicular to the ground.

c. $\sqrt{225 - 144} = \sqrt{81} = 9$ ft

d. Possible answer: She could use a 5-foot pole that would touch the barn 4 ft high and rest on the ground 3 ft from the base of the barn.

56. 78 units. Triangle CDB is similar to triangle ABC, because both have angle B and a right angle. Because $12^2 + 5^2 = 169$, the length of side BC is $\sqrt{169} = 13$ units. The leg of length 5 units on the small triangle corresponds with the leg of length 13 units on triangle ABC, so the scale factor from triangle CDB to triangle ABC is $\frac{13}{5}$, or 2.6. Multiplying the side lengths of triangle CDB by 2.6, side AC has length $12 \cdot 2.6 = 31.2$ units and side BA has length $13 \cdot 2.6 = 33.8$ units. The perimeter of triangle ABC is thus $13 + 31.2 + 33.8 = 78$ units. (**Note:** Students may also calculate that triangle CDB has a perimeter of $5 + 12 + 13 = 30$ and then apply the scale factor to find that the perimeter of triangle ABC is $30 \cdot 2.6 = 78$.)

57. a. Using the Pythagorean Theorem, the length of half of the edge of the base is 3 units, so the edge length of the base is 6 units. Therefore, the base area is 36 units^2.

b. The surface is made up of 4 congruent triangles plus a base. Each triangle has area $(\frac{1}{2})(6)(4) = 12$ units^2. So the surface area is $36 + 4(12) = 84$ units^2.

c. The height of the pyramid is found from the right triangle with sides 3 units (half of the base edge) and 4 units (the slant height). We need to solve $3^2 + h^2 = 4^2$. h is $\sqrt{7}$ units, or about 2.65 units.

d. $(\frac{1}{3})(36)(2.65) \approx 31.8$ units^3.

58. a. 31.81 in.^{3}. Because the diameter is 4.5 in., the radius is 2.25 in. The height is 6 in., so the volume is $\frac{1}{3}\pi(2.25)^2(6) \approx 31.81$ in.^{3}

b. 26π in.^{3}. $7^2 = r^2 + 6^2$, so $r = \sqrt{13}$ in., or about 3.6 in. So the volume is $\frac{1}{3}\pi(\sqrt{13})^2(6) = 26\pi$ in.^{3}, or about 81.7 in.^{3}

Possible Answers to Mathematical Reflections

1. The Pythagorean Theorem is useful for finding the length of one side of a right triangle if you know the lengths of the other two sides.

An example of this is finding the distance between two points when the coordinates of the points are known. We connect the points with a line segment and then use the segment as the hypotenuse of a right triangle. We draw the two legs, find their lengths, and then find the sum of the squares of the lengths. The distance between the two points is the square root of this sum.

Another example is finding the length of the diagonal d of a rectangle. If the side lengths of the rectangle are a and b, then the Pythagorean Theorem tells us $d^2 = a^2 + b^2$, or $d = \sqrt{a^2 + b^2}$.

2. In a 30-60-90 triangle, the length of the side opposite the 30° angle is half the length of the hypotenuse. The length of the longer leg is $\sqrt{3}$ times the length of the leg opposite the 30° angle. (**Note:** In a 30-60-90 triangle, if the leg opposite the 30° angle has length a, then the hypotenuse has length $2a$. So, the longer leg has length $\sqrt{4a^2 - a^2} = \sqrt{3a^2} = a\sqrt{3}$.)

Answers to Looking Back and Looking Ahead

1. a. 12.5 units^2

b. $2.5\sqrt{2}$ units, or $\sqrt{12.5}$, or approximately 3.536 units

c. 10 units, $5\sqrt{2}$ units, and $5\sqrt{2}$ units

d. Triangle B: scale factor is 1 (in other words, triangles A and B are congruent);

Triangle F: scale factor from F to A is 2 and from A to F is $\frac{1}{2}$;

Triangle D: scale factor from D to A is 2 and from A to D is $\frac{1}{2}$;

Triangle G: scale factor from G to A is $\sqrt{2}$ and from A to G is $\frac{1}{\sqrt{2}}$

2. a. The length of the side opposite a 30° angle in a 30-60-90 triangle is half the length of the hypotenuse. Thus the wire is attached to the ground 30 ft from the base of the tower.

b. Use the Pythagorean Theorem to find the length of the other leg. The height of the tower is $30\sqrt{3}$ or approximately 52 ft.

3. You can determine the length of a side of any square by finding the square root of its area. Students may have used this strategy to find the side length of Square E in part (a) of Problem 1.

4. Possible answer: Form a right triangle whose hypotenuse is the line segment. The lengths of the legs are the positive difference in the x-coordinates of the endpoints and positive difference in the y-coordinates of the endpoints. Once you know the lengths of the legs, apply the Pythagorean Theorem to find the length of the hypotenuse, which is the line segment. If you forget the Pythagorean Theorem, you can build a square whose length is the given line segment. Find the area of the square and then take the square root of the area to find the length of the line segment.

5. a. The triangle is a right triangle. Therefore, the Pythagorean relationship applies: The sum of the area of the squares on the legs is equal to the area of the square on the hypotenuse.

b. Because the triangle in Figure 2 is not a right triangle, the Pythagorean Theorem does not apply.

6. a. The length of the diagonal of a square is the square root of the sum of the squares of two of the side lengths. If d is the length of the diagonal and s is the side length, then
$$d = \sqrt{s^2 + s^2} = \sqrt{2s^2} = s\sqrt{2}.$$

b. The length of the diagonal of a rectangle is the square root of the sum of the squares of the length and width. If d is the length of the diagonal and s and t are the width and length, then $d = \sqrt{s^2 + t^2}$.

c. The length of the hypotenuse of a right triangle is the square root of the sum of the squares of the lengths of the legs. If c is the length of the hypotenuse and s and t are the lengths of the legs, then $c = \sqrt{s^2 + t^2}$.

d. The height of an equilateral triangle is the square root of the difference of the square of a side length and the square of half a side length. If d is the height and s is the side length, then $d = \sqrt{s^2 - (\frac{s}{2})^2}$ (or $d = \frac{s}{2}\sqrt{3}$ based on 30-60-90 triangle properties).

e. The length of one side of a right triangle is the square root of the difference of the squares of the hypotenuse and the other side length. If a is unknown leg length, t is the known leg length, and h is the length of the hypotenuse, then $a = \sqrt{h^2 - t^2}$.

For the Teacher In Problem 6, students may describe each process as three steps. For example in part (a), they may say:

- Take the square of two side lengths of the square.
- Add these two squares.
- Take the square root of the sum.

Looking Back and Looking Ahead

Unit Review

While working on problems in this unit, you extended your skill in using a coordinate system to locate points and figures. Then, by studying patterns in the side lengths and areas of squares on dot grids, you learned the Pythagorean Theorem. You used this property of right triangles to solve a variety of practical problems, some of which involved irrational numbers.

Go Online
PHSchool.com
For: Vocabulary Review Puzzle
Web Code: apj-2051

Use Your Understanding: The Pythagorean Theorem

Test your understanding of the Pythagorean Theorem and its relationship to area, lengths of line segments, and irrational numbers by solving the following problems.

1. The diagram shows a Chinese tangram puzzle on a 10-by-10 grid.

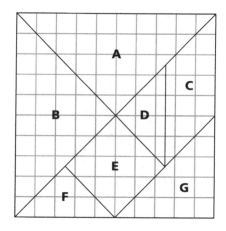

   a. What is the area of shape E?

   b. What is the length of each side of shape E?

   c. What are the lengths of the sides of triangle A?

   d. Name all the triangles that are similar to triangle A. In each case, give a scale factor for the similarity relationship.

Notes _____

_____

_____

_____

2. A 60-foot piece of wire is strung between the top of a tower and the ground, making a 30-60-90 triangle.

Tower
Wire
60°

a. How far from the center of the base of the tower is the wire attached to the ground?

b. How high is the tower?

Explain Your Reasoning

When you present work based on the Pythagorean relationship, you should be able to justify your calculations and conclusions.

3. How can you find the side length of a square if you know its area?

4. How can you find the length of a segment joining two points on a coordinate grid?

5. The diagrams below show squares drawn on the sides of triangles.

Figure 1   **Figure 2**

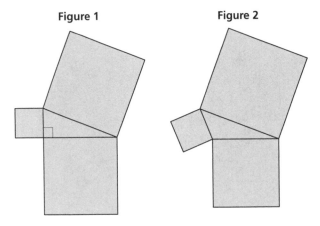

a. In Figure 1, what is the relationship among the areas of the squares?

b. Explain why the relationship you describe in part (a) is not true for Figure 2.

Notes _____

_____

_____

_____

6. Explain with words and symbols how to use the Pythagorean Theorem to find the

   a. length of a diagonal of a square with side length s.

   b. length of a diagonal of a rectangle with side lengths s and t.

   c. length of the hypotenuse of a right triangle with legs of lengths s and t.

   d. height of an equilateral triangle with side length s.

   e. length of one leg of a triangle when the lengths of the hypotenuse and the other leg are h and t, respectively.

Look Ahead

You will use the properties of right triangles you discovered in this unit, including the Pythagorean Theorem, in many future *Connected Mathematics* units, and in the math, science, and technology courses you take in high school and college.

Looking Back and Looking Ahead   **67**

Notes _____

_____

_____

_____

C

conjecture A guess about a pattern or relationship based on observations.

conjetura Suposición acerca de un patron o relación, basada en observaciones.

H

hypotenuse The side of a right triangle that is opposite the right angle. The hypotenuse is the longest side of a right triangle. In the triangle below, the side labeled c is the hypotenuse.

hipotenusa El lado de un triángulo rectángulo que está opuesto al ángulo recto. La hipotenusa es el lado más largo de un triángulo rectángulo. En el triángulo de abajo, el lado rotulado c es la hipotenusa.

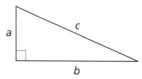

I

irrational number A number that cannot be written as a fraction with a numerator and a denominator that are integers. The decimal representation of an irrational number never ends and never shows a repeating pattern of a fixed number of digits. The numbers $\sqrt{2}$, $\sqrt{3}$, $\sqrt{5}$, and π are examples of irrational numbers.

número irracional Un número que no puede escribirse como una fracción con un numerador y un denominador que sean enteros. La representación decimal de un número irracional nunca termina y nunca muestra un patrón de dígitos que se repite. Los números $\sqrt{2}$, $\sqrt{3}$, $\sqrt{5}$, y π son ejemplos de números irracionales.

L

legs The sides of a right triangle that are adjacent to the right angle. In the triangle above, the sides labeled a and b are the legs.

catetos Los lados de un triángulo rectángulo que son adyacentes al ángulo recto. En el triángulo de arriba, los lados a y b son los catetos.

P

perpendicular Forming a right angle. For example, the sides of a right triangle that form the right angle are perpendicular.

perpendicular Que forma un ángulo recto. Por ejemplo, los lados de un triángulo rectángulo que forman el ángulo recto son perpendiculares.

Pythagorean Theorem A statement about the relationship among the lengths of the sides of a right triangle. The theorem states that if a and b are the lengths of the legs of a right triangle and c is the length of the hypotenuse, then $a^2 + b^2 = c^2$.

Teorema de Pitágoras Un enunciado acerca de la relación que existe entre las longitudes de los lados de un triángulo rectángulo. El teorema enuncia que si a y b son las longitudes de los catetos de un triángulo rectángulo y c es la longitud de la hipotenusa, entonces $a^2 + b^2 = c^2$.

Notes

_____

_____

_____

_____

rational number A number that can be written as a fraction with a numerator and a denominator that are integers. The decimal representation of a rational number either ends or repeats. Examples of rational numbers are $\frac{1}{2}$, $\frac{78}{91}$, 7, 0.2, and 0.191919. . . .

número racional Un número que puede escribirse como una fracción con un numerador y un denominador que son enteros. La representación decimal de un número racional termina o bien se repite. Ejemplos de números racionales son $\frac{1}{2}$, $\frac{78}{91}$, 7, 0.2 y 0.191919. . . .

real numbers The set of all rational numbers and all irrational numbers. The number line represents the set of real numbers.

números reales El conjunto de todos los números racionales y todos los números irracionales. La recta numérica representa el conjunto de los números reales.

repeating decimal A decimal with a pattern of a fixed number of digits that repeats forever, such as 0.3333333. . . and 0.73737373. . . . Repeating decimals are rational numbers.

decimal periódico Un decimal con un patrón de dígitos que se repite indefinidamente, como 0.3333333. . . y 0.73737373. . . . Los decimales que se repiten son números racionales.

square root If $A = s^2$, then s is the square root of A. For example, -3 and 3 are square roots of 9 because $3 \cdot 3 = 9$ and $-3 \cdot -3 = 9$. The $\sqrt{}$ symbol is used to denote the positive square root. So, we write $\sqrt{9} = 3$. The positive square root of a number is the side length of a square that has that number as its area. So, you can draw a segment of length $\sqrt{5}$ by drawing a square with an area of 5, and the side length of the square will be $\sqrt{5}$.

raíz cuadrada Si $A = s^2$, entonces s es la raíz cuadrada de A. Por ejemplo, -3 y 3 son raíces cuadradas de 9 porque $3 \cdot 3 = 9$ y $-3 \cdot -3 = 9$. El símbolo $\sqrt{}$ se usa para indicar la raíz cuadrada positiva. Por eso, escribimos $\sqrt{9} = 3$. La raíz cuadrada positiva de un número es la longitud del lado de un cuadrado que tiene dicho número como su área. Entonces, puedes dibujar un segmento de longitud $\sqrt{5}$ dibujando un cuadrado con un área de 5 y la longitud del lado del cuadrado será $\sqrt{5}$.

T

terminating decimal A decimal that ends, or terminates, such as 0.5 or 0.125. Terminating decimals are rational numbers.

decimal finito Un decimal que se acaba o termina, como 0.5 ó 0.125. Los decimales finitos son números racionales.

English/Spanish Glossary **69**

Notes _____

_____

_____

_____

Academic Vocabulary

The following terms are important to your understanding of the mathematics in this unit. Knowing and using these words will help you in thinking, reasoning, representing, communicating your ideas, and making connections across ideas. When these words make sense to you, the investigations and problems will make more sense as well.

A

analyze To think about and understand facts and details about a given set of information. Analyzing can involve providing a written summary supported by factual information, a diagram, chart, table, or any combination of these.

related terms: explain, describe, justify

Sample: Analyze the squares. How is the side length related to the area?

The first square has an area of 9 units² and a side length of 3 units. The side length is the square root of the area. The second square has an area of 4 full units² and 8 half-units² for a total of 8 units². The side length is the square root of the area or $\sqrt{8}$ units.

analizar Pensar acerca de y comprender hechos y detalles sobre un conjunto determinado de información. Analizar puede implicar proporcionar un resumen escrito apoyado por información real, un diagrama, una gráfica, una tabla o cualquier combinación de éstos.

términos relacionados: explicar, describir, justificar

Ejemplo: Analiza los cuadrados. ¿Cómo se relaciona la longitud del lado con el área?

El primer cuadrado tiene un área de 9 unidades² y una longitud del lado de 3 unidades. La longitud del lado es la raíz cuadrada del área. El segundo cuadrado tiene un área de 4 unidades² completas y 8 unidades² medias que hacen un total de 8 unidades². La longitud del lado es la raíz cuadrada del área u $\sqrt{8}$ unidades.

E

estimate To find an approximate answer.

related terms: approximate, guess

Sample: Estimate $\sqrt{10}$.

I know that $\sqrt{9} = 3$ and $\sqrt{16} = 4$. Since $\sqrt{10}$ is much closer to $\sqrt{9}$ than it is to $\sqrt{16}$, my estimate will be closer to 3 than to 4. I estimate $\sqrt{10}$ as about 3.2.

estimar Hallar una respuesta aproximada.

términos relacionados: aproximar, conjeturar

Ejemplo: Estima $\sqrt{10}$.

Sé que $\sqrt{9} = 3$ y $\sqrt{16} = 4$. Puesto que $\sqrt{10}$ está mucho más cerca de $\sqrt{9}$ que de $\sqrt{16}$, mi estimación estaría más cercana a 3 que a 4. Estimo que $\sqrt{10}$ es aproximadamente de 3.2.

70 Looking for Pythagoras

Notes _____

_____

_____

_____

find To use the given information and any related facts, to determine or calculate a value. You may use mathematical algorithms, properties, formulas, or any combination of these, as well as other mathematical strategies, when finding a value.

related terms: calculate, discover, determine

Sample: Find the area of triangle *ABC*.

I can count the number of unit squares. △ABC has an area of 4.5 unit squares. I can also find the area by using the formula $A = \frac{1}{2}bh$, where the base and the height of the triangle are each 3 units in length.

$A = \frac{1}{2}(3)(3) = 4.5$ square units

hallar Usar la información dada y cualesquiera datos relacionados para determinar o calcular un valor. Puedes usar algoritmos matemáticos, propiedades, fórmulas o cualquier combinación de éstos, así como otras estrategias matemáticas, cuando hallas un valor.

términos relacionado: calcular, descubrir, determinar

Ejemplo: Halla el área del triángulo *ABC*.

Puedo contar el número de unidades cuadradas. El △ABC tiene un área de 4.5 unidades cuadradas. Puedo hallar el área usando la fórmula $A = \frac{1}{2}ba$, donde la base y la altura del triángulo miden 3 unidades de longitud respectivamente.

$A = \frac{1}{2}(3)(3) = 4.5$ square units

observe To notice or to examine carefully one or more characteristics of a particular object.

related terms: notice, examine, note, see

Sample: What do you observe about the sum of the squares of the lengths of the legs of the right triangle in relationship to the length of the hypotenuse?

If I square the length of the hypotenuse, I get $5^2 = 25$. This is equal to the sum of the squares of the lengths of the legs of the triangle $3^2 + 4^2 = 9 + 16 = 25$.

The area of the square built on the hypotenuse is equal to the sum of the areas of the squares built on the two legs of the right triangle.

observar Notar o examinar con cuidado una o más características de un objeto particular.

términos relacionados: k notar, examinar, señalar, ver

Ejemplo: ¿Qué observas sobre la suma de los cuadrados de las longitudes de los catetos del triángulo rectángulo con relación a la longitud de la hipotenusa?

Si elevo al cuadrado la longitud de la hipotenusa, obtengo $5^2 = 25$. Esto es igual a la suma de los cuadrados de las longitudes de los catetos del triángulo $3^2 + 4^2 = 9 + 16 = 25$.

El área del cuadrado construido sobre la hipotenusa es igual a la suma de las áreas de los cuadrados construidos sobre los dos catetos del triángulo rectángulo.

Academic Vocabulary **71**

STUDENT PAGE

Notes _____

_____

_____

_____

Index

Notes

_____

_____

_____

_____

Index

STUDENT PAGE

Notes _____

_____

_____

_____

Acknowledgments

Team Credits

The people who made up the **Connected Mathematics 2** team—representing editorial, editorial services, design services, and production services—are listed below. Bold type denotes core team members.

Leora Adler, Judith Buice, Kerry Cashman, Patrick Culleton, Sheila DeFazio, Katie Hallahan, Richard Heater, **Barbara Hollingdale, Jayne Holman,** Karen Holtzman, **Etta Jacobs,** Christine Lee, Carolyn Lock, Catherine Maglio, **Dotti Marshall,** Rich McMahon, Eve Melnechuk, Kristin Mingrone, Terri Mitchell, **Marsha Novak,** Irene Rubin, Donna Russo, Robin Samper, Siri Schwartzman, **Nancy Smith,** Emily Soltanoff, **Mark Tricca,** Paula Vergith, Roberta Warshaw, Helen Young

Additional Credits

Diana Bonfilio, Mairead Reddin, Michael Torocsik, nSight, Inc.

Technical Illustration

WestWords, Inc.

Cover Design

tom white.images

Photos

2, Erich Lessing/Art Resource, NY; **3,** Yellow Dog Productions/Getty Images, Inc.; **5,** Francis Miller/Time Life Pictures; **6,** Richard T Nowitz/Getty Images, Inc.; **15,** Comstock Images/Getty Images, Inc.; **20,** Richard Haynes; **27,** Richard Haynes; **28,** Catherine Ledner/Getty Images, Inc.; **33,** The Art Archive/Museo Capitolino Rome/Dagli Orti (A); **36,** Erich Lessing/Art Resource, NY; **41 both,** Richard Haynes; **44,** Richard Haynes; **46,** Patrick Ben Luke Syder/Lonely Planet Images; **49,** AP Photo/Jerry Laizure; **50,** Library of Congress, Prints and Photographs Division, LOT 13163-09, no. 1; **52,** Courtesy Everett Collection/ Everett Collection; **54,** Dennis MacDonald/Photo Edit

Data Sources

Did You Know quote on page 52 is an excerpt from *The Wizard of Oz* granted courtesy of Warner Bros. Entertainment Inc. All Rights Reserved. Copyright © 1939.

Note: Every effort has been made to locate the copyright owner of the material reprinted in this book. Omissions brought to our attention will be corrected in subsequent editions.

STUDENT PAGE

74 Looking for Pythagoras

Notes

Dot Paper

Centimeter Grid Paper

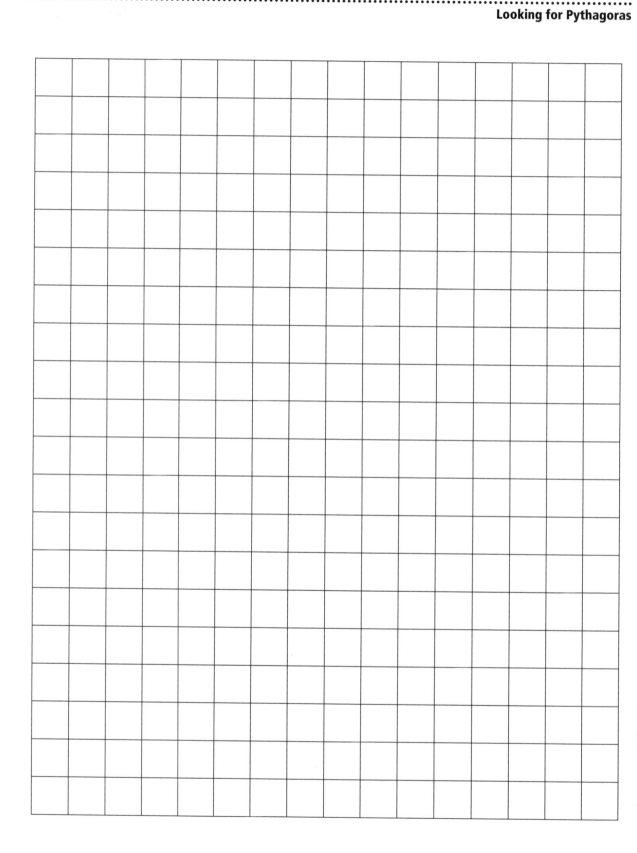

Labsheet 1.1

Maps of Euclid

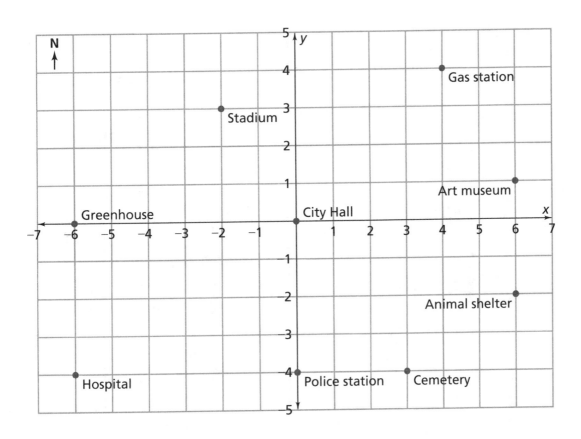

Labsheet 1.2

Planning Parks

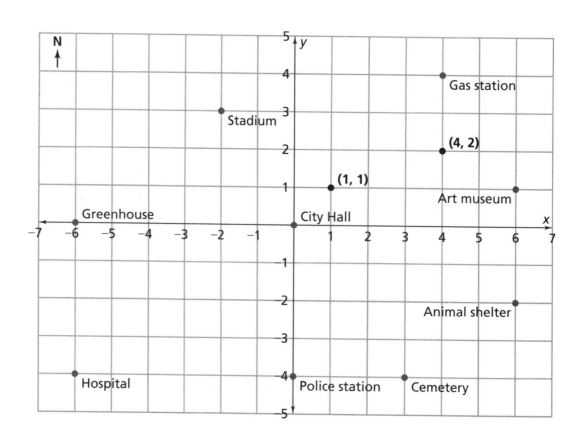

Labsheet 1.3

Figures for Problem 1.3

1.

2.

3.

4.

5.

6.

7.

8.

9.

10.

Labsheet 1ACE Exercises 15–25

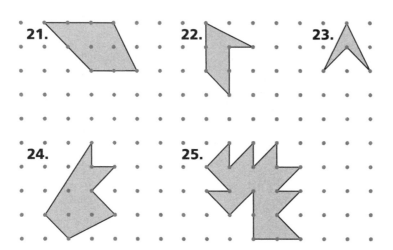

Labsheet 2.1

5 Dot-by-5 Dot Grids

Labsheet 2.3

Enclosed 5 Dot-by-5 Dot Grids

Labsheet 3.2A

Puzzle Frames and Puzzle Pieces, Set A

Frames

Puzzle Pieces

Labsheet 3.2B

Puzzle Frames and Puzzle Pieces, Set B

Frames

Puzzle Pieces

Labsheet 3.2C

Puzzle Frames and Puzzle Pieces, Set C

Frames

Puzzle Pieces

Labsheet 3.3

Points on a Grid

Labsheet 4.1

The Wheel of Theodorus

Labsheet 4.4

Questions A–C

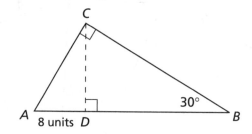

PACING: _____

Mathematical Goals

_____
_____
_____
_____

Launch

_____
_____
_____
_____
_____
_____
_____
_____

Materials

Explore

_____
_____
_____
_____
_____
_____
_____
_____

Materials

Summarize

_____
_____
_____
_____
_____
_____
_____

Materials

Glossary

C

conjecture A guess about a pattern or relationship based on observations.

H

hypotenuse The side of a right triangle that is opposite the right angle. The hypotenuse is the longest side of a right triangle. In the triangle below, the side labeled c is the hypotenuse.

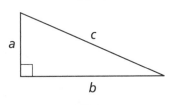

I

irrational number A number that cannot be written as a fraction with a numerator and a denominator that are integers. The decimal representation of an irrational number never ends and never shows a repeating pattern of a fixed number of digits. The numbers $\sqrt{2}$, $\sqrt{3}$, $\sqrt{5}$, and π are examples of irrational numbers.

L

legs The sides of a right triangle that are adjacent to the right angle. In the triangle above, the sides labeled a and b are the legs.

P

perpendicular Forming a right angle. For example, the sides of a right triangle that form the right angle are perpendicular.

Pythagorean Theorem A statement about the relationship among the lengths of the sides of a right triangle. The theorem states that if a and b are the lengths of the legs of a right triangle and c is the length of the hypotenuse, then $a^2 + b^2 = c^2$.

R

rational number A number that can be written as a fraction with a numerator and a denominator that are integers. The decimal representation of a rational number either ends or repeats. Examples of rational numbers are $\frac{1}{2}$, $\frac{78}{91}$, 7, 0.2, and 0.191919. . . .

real numbers The set of all rational numbers and all irrational numbers. The number line represents the set of real numbers.

repeating decimal A decimal with a pattern of a fixed number of digits that repeats forever, such as 0.3333333. . . and 0.73737373. . . . Repeating decimals are rational numbers.

S

square root If $A = s^2$, then s is the square root of A. For example, -3 and 3 are square roots of 9 because $3 \cdot 3 = 9$ and $-3 \cdot -3 = 9$. The $\sqrt{}$ symbol is used to denote the positive square root. So, we write $\sqrt{9} = 3$. The positive square root of a number is the side length of a square that has that number as its area. So, you can draw a segment of length $\sqrt{5}$ by drawing a square with an area of 5, and the side length of the square will be $\sqrt{5}$.

T

terminating decimal A decimal that ends, or terminates, such as 0.5 or 0.125. Terminating decimals are rational numbers.

Index

Acknowledgments

Team Credits

The people who made up the **Connected Mathematics 2** team—representing editorial, editorial services, design services, and production services—are listed below. Bold type denotes core team members.

Leora Adler, Judith Buice, Kerry Cashman, Patrick Culleton, Sheila DeFazio, Richard Heater, **Barbara Hollingdale, Jayne Holman,** Karen Holtzman, **Etta Jacobs,** Christine Lee, Carolyn Lock, Catherine Maglio, **Dotti Marshall,** Rich McMahon, Eve Melnechuk, Kristin Mingrone, Terri Mitchell, **Marsha Novak,** Irene Rubin, Donna Russo, Robin Samper, Siri Schwartzman, **Nancy Smith,** Emily Soltanoff, **Mark Tricca,** Paula Vergith, Roberta Warshaw, Helen Young

Additional Credits

Diana Bonfilio, Mairead Reddin, Michael Torocsik, nSight, Inc.

Technical Illustration

Schawk, Inc.

Cover Design

tom white.images